FROM THE
TOWER WINDOW

OF

MY BOOK HOUSE

EDITED BY

OLIVE BEAUPRÉ MILLER

PUBLISHERS

THE BOOK HOUSE for CHILDREN

CHICAGO

THIRTY-FOURTH PRINTING, 1951

PRINTED IN U. S. A.

PREFACE

AS the title suggests, "From the Tower Window" is primarily the book of romantic as well as heroic adventure, and the design has been, first of all, to include in it stories from all the great national epics. As the folk tales reflect the commonplace, homely, everyday life of the various nations and peoples, so the highest, loftiest, noblest, most stirring and deeply moving thoughts of the peoples have been expressed in their various long epic poems. From generation to generation these tales were told or sung by wandering bards in hall and castle or to a crowd on the street, until at last, some poet appeared, of sufficient genius to write down the tale and give it permanent form in the peculiar style and rhythm of his own country. In these massive old epics, with their splendid seriousness and dignity, their rousing stir of activity, their rhythmic flow of line, their numberless passages of great and lofty beauty, we find the finest literature of each country.

So "From the Tower Window" brings to older boys and girls the story of these epics, told, so far as possible, in the very style, spirit and feeling of the original. Here we have the romantic tale of "Sir Beaumains, the Kitchen Knight," from the English cycle of legends concerning King Arthur and his Round Table, and we have "How Beowulf Delivered Heorot," from the earliest English epic, "Beowulf," originally written in Anglo-Saxon. We have also "The Home-Coming of Odysseus," retold from the Greek epic, "The Odyssey," of Homer; "The Wanderings of Aeneas," the great epic of the Romans, retold from the Latin of Virgil; "Cuculain, the Irish Hound," from tales of the ancient Gaelic bards; "Frithjof, the Viking," from the Norse saga of "Frithjof;" "The Song of Roland," from the great French epic of that name; "The Story of the Cid," from the Spanish; "Kalevala, Land of Heroes," from the Finnish epic, "Kalevala;" "The Word of Igor's Armament," from an old Russian epic; "The Exile of Rama," from "The Ramayana," the sacred poem of India; "The Story of Rustem, the

Hero of Persia," from "The Shah-Nameh" (Book of Kings) by Firdusi; and "Lohengrin," from the epic German material on which Richard Wagner based his opera, Lohengrin.

Thus the great epics of the world are given to boys and girls before they enter high school but, as basic literature, they remain of interest to high school students and adults as well.

"From the Tower Window" also gives the older children another story from Shakespeare, "As You Like It," and "Joseph and His Brethren," from the Bible. Furthermore, it contains some of the choicest stories from actual history, presenting the most characteristic and beloved heroes of various nations—Robert Bruce from the Scotch, combined with the rousing Scotch poems of Robert Burns and Sir Walter Scott; Joan of Arc from the French and William Tell from the Swiss. And grouped with these stories is "The Children's Crusade," which concerns the adventures of that army of children from France and Germany who set forth as crusaders for the Holy Land in the year 1212, under their two boy leaders, Stephen and Nicholas. So magic did the appeal of Stephen and Nicholas seem to be in charming children to leave home and follow them that this true story gave rise to the legend of the "Pied Piper of Hamelin," as told in Browning's poem of that name.

The only fictional story about children in Volume Ten is "Richard Feverel and the Hay-Rick," by George Meredith, one of the best stories of boyhood in all literature, and done by one of the real masters of English fiction. The story of Richard's whipping at the hands of Farmer Blaize, his anger, his revenge, and the consequent struggle with his conscience, resulting at last in victory for his conscience, constitutes an adventure within a boy's soul, that has few parallels in literature.

CONTENTS

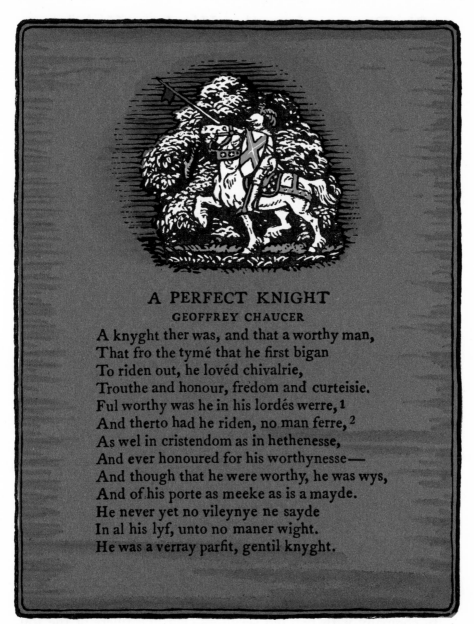

A PERFECT KNIGHT
GEOFFREY CHAUCER

A knyght ther was, and that a worthy man,
That fro the tymé that he first bigan
To riden out, he lovéd chivalrie,
Trouthe and honour, fredom and curteisie.
Ful worthy was he in his lordés werre, 1
And therto had he riden, no man ferre, 2
As wel in cristendom as in hethenesse,
And ever honoured for his worthynesse—
And though that he were worthy, he was wys,
And of his porte as meeke as is a mayde.
He never yet no vileynye ne sayde
In al his lyf, unto no maner wight.
He was a verray parfit, gentil knyght.

1wars. 2farther.

Sir Beaumains, the Kitchen Knight

A Legend of the Round Table

The King will follow Christ, and we the King
In whom high God hath breathed a secret thing.
Fall, battle axe, and flash brand! Let the King reign!

It befell in the days of King Arthur, that there dwelt in Ork-ney with the old King Lot and Bel'li-cent, his queen, one last tall son, young Ga'reth, his elder brothers being gone to serve the King at Cam'e-lot. And Bellicent, yearning in her heart to keep her last born by her side to cheer the empty lone-liness of her vast reechoing halls, would never yield consent that Gareth should leave his father and herself to follow Arthur. Still, Gareth never ceased from longing that he too might go to Cam'e-lot to serve the King,—to ride abroad redressing human wrongs, and wiping all things base from out the world.

"Ah, mother," he would cry, "how can you hold me tethered to your side? Man am I grown, a man's work must I do. I must follow the Christ, the King,—live pure, speak true, right wrong, follow the King. Else wherefore was I born?"

So Gareth besought his mother continually until at last Queen Bellicent was wearied of his prayers and cried:

"Go, if thou wilt. But an thou goest I shall hold this one requirement fast. Thou shalt disguise thyself as a kitchen-knave and serve amongst the scullions, nor ever tell thine own right name for a twelvemonth and a day."

By this request the Queen thought secretly to keep her Gareth by her side, for never did she dream that he would still persist, and take his way to Arthur's service through such mean and lowly vas-salage. A moment Gareth stood silent. Then he cried, "Though I be but a thrall in person, I shall still be free in soul! And I shall see the jousts." And so he went.

In company with two old servitors clad like tillers of the soil,

8

FROM THE TOWER WINDOW

he journeyed to Camelot. And there at last, upon the royal mount, he saw the city rising, her spires and turrets pricking through the silver mists and flashing in the sun. Beneath the splendid carven gate he entered in, and ever and anon a knight with flashing arms would pass him by. From bower and casement lovely ladies glanced and through the busy streets a healthful people went about the business of the day in such security as comes from sure protection of a strong and gracious king.

Thus Gareth passed on to King Arthur's hall and there beheld the great King seated on his throne in all the majesty of mighty manhood, his tall knights ranged about, their eyes clear shining with the light of honor and affection and of faith in their great King. Thither came many more to make requests or seek for justice of the King, but in his turn young Gareth stood before the throne and cried: "A boon, sir King! I beg thee that thou give me place to serve among thy kitchen knaves a twelvemonth and a day, nor ask my name."

"Fair son," said Arthur, "thou seemest a goodly youth and worth a goodlier boon. But if thou askest nothing more, then have this, thy request. Serve under my steward, Sir Kay."

Now Sir Kay was a surly man of sour and evil temper.

"I undertake this fellow is a villain born!" he cried. "Doubtless he hath broken from some abbey or castle where he had not beef and brewis enow! But an he do well his work for me, he shall be fed like any hog."

"Nay," cried Sir Lancelot. "Methinks thou dost not truly judge the lad. He looks like one of noble lineage who hides some secret in his scullion's clothes."

"Noble lineage!" scoffed Sir Kay. "An he were noble, he would ask for horse and armor. Noble, forsooth! Sir Beaumains, Sir Fair-hands! Since thou hast no other name, I dub thee Fair-hands. Off with thee to thy knightly post beside the spit, Sir Fair-hands!"

Stories of King Arthur, hero of the struggle between Britons and invading Anglo-Saxons in the 6th Century, were told in Wales, in the Mabinogion; in Germany, by Wolfram von Eschenbach; in France, by Crétien de Troyes.

Thus it was young Gareth came by the name of Beaumains, which meaneth Fair-hands. Obedient to Sir Kay, he served within the sooty kitchen, turning the spit, drawing water, hewing wood, washing the greasy pots and kettles, and sleeping at night midst grimy kitchen knaves. And ever Sir Kay would harry him and hustle him and mock him beyond all others of his fellows. Yet for a twelvemonth and a day Gareth endured in patience and without complaint, and sometimes when there were jousts, Sir Kay would nod him leave to go. Forgetful then of aught besides, he watched the combats eagerly, and ever Sir Lancelot and others of the courtliest knights bespoke him fair, reverencing in spite of all his kitchen clothes, the nobleness writ on his face.

So passed the time till Gareth had fulfilled in all good faith his vow unto his mother. Then he sought the King alone and told him all his tale.

"O King," he cried. "Make me thy knight in secret. Let no man know my name until I make a name. But give me the first quest!"

"Make thee my knight?" the King spake thoughtfully. "My knights are sworn to vows of utter hardihood, of utter purity and gentleness, of uttermost obedience to the King."

But Gareth in full fire of youthful spirits answered, "O my King, for hardiness I promise thee. For uttermost obedience make demand of Kay, no gentle master to have served."

Whereat the King, loving his lusty youthhood, yielded half unwillingly. "So be it! I will make thee my knight in secret."

That same day there came into the hall, attended by her page, a lovely damsel with a brow of may-blossom and a cheek of apple-blossom and a nose tip-tilted like the petal of a flower.

"O King," she cried, "Lynette's my name. I come of noble lineage. Pray give me succor for my sister, the lady Ly'o-nors' who by a savage tyrant is shut up within her castle. About her dwelling place a river runs in three great loops and at each pass

During the twelfth century, Geoffrey of Monmouth wrote some of the King Arthur tales in Latin. In 1469, Sir Thomas Malory's *Morte d'Arthur* appeared, translated from old French poems. Tennyson's *Idylls of the King* were based on these legends.

FROM THE TOWER WINDOW

across the stream, three hideous brothers of the tyrant stand,—
all men that ride abroad to do but what they will, nor make
acknowledgment of any law or king, and hate the very name of
Arthur. These three are horrible enough, but he, the fourth, who
keeps the last ward by the castle itself, a huge man-beast is he
of boundless savagery. He always rideth armed in black and
bears a ghastly skeleton on his arms. Such are those four that
hold my sister prisoner to force her, will or nill, to wed with one
of them. So am I come to thee to beg the best of all thy knights,
Sir Lancelot, to save her from the clutches of these beasts."

Hereat rose up the kitchen-knave, Beaumains, and called
with kindling eyes, above the throng, "A boon, Sir King! Grant
me the quest!"

Much wondered all in that vast hall to hear a wretched
scullion speak like this, but Arthur mindful of his promise, said,
"The quest is thine! I grant it to thee! Go!"

Then was the damsel wroth.

"Fie on thee, King," she cried. "I asked for thy chief knight
and thou hast given me but a kitchen knave." And she in anger
took her horse and fled away.

With that, came one and told Beaumains that horse and armor
stood ready for him—the gift of Arthur. And when he was
armed therein, there were but few so goodly men as he. The
people marveled, and the kitchen thralls, pressing from out the
kitchen to see one who had worked more lustily than any among
them, mounted and in arms, threw up their caps and shouted
loud. Through midst of all this shouting Gareth rode away.

As he drew near Lynette, he cried, "Damsel, the quest is
mine. Lead and I follow."

But Lynette with petulant thumb and finger nipped her
slender nose—"Away!" she shrilled. "Thou smellest all of
kitchen grease! And look behind! There cometh he, Sir Kay,
thy master, to reclaim his kitchen-knave!"

Tennyson's *Song of King Arthur's Knights*, "Blow Trumpet for the World Is White," has been set to music by Nevin.
Wagner's operas, *Parsifal* and *Lohengrin*, and MacDowell's symphonic poem, *Lancelot and Elaine*, are based on
these legends.

For Kay, angered at seeing his underling thus sent on knightly quest, had come pursuing with hot haste, in confidence that he should prick the bubble of the young lad's pride by hurling him at once into the dust and so return him to his kitchen vassalage.

And as he rode, the steward bawled, "Ho, Sir Beaumains, Sir Fair-hands, wait. Know ye not me, your master?"

"Master no more!" quoth Gareth. "Thou art the most ungentle knight in Arthur's court!"

Therewith Sir Kay ran furiously upon him. Sir Gareth met the charge, but at the first shock of encounter, Sir Kay fell to the ground so stunned he could not rise. Then Gareth once again cried to the damsel, "Lead and I follow!"

Fast she fled away at full speed of her horse and when Sir Gareth won her side, she cried, "Weenest thou that I think the more of thee because through some mischance thou hast over-thrown thy master? Nay, broach-turner and dish-washer, to me thou smellest all of kitchen as before."

"Damsel," said Sir Gareth, "say to me what ye list, I will not leave you whatsoever ye say, for I have undertaken of King Arthur for to achieve your adventure and I shall finish it unto the end."

Maddened at his good words, the damsel flashed away again down the long avenues of the boundless wood. So they rode on until the dusk when from a hill-top they espied below a gloomy hollow, in the deeps whereof a mere, red as the round eye of an owl, glared in the half dead sunset. And there came flying toward them from the wood a serving man in great affright.

"O my lord," he cried to Gareth, "help me! For hereby are six thieves that have taken my master and bound him fast. They hate him for that it hath been his work to keep this forest ever free from thieves, and even now they are about to slay him."

"Bring me thither," Sir Gareth said.

Into the darkening pines they plunged and there, amid black shadows, saw six tall men haling a seventh along with a stone about his neck to drown him in the mere. Sir Gareth rode full boldly on the thieves. One at his first stroke he struck to earth and then another and a third. Thereat the other three in terror, fled, and Gareth was left master of the field. Right courteously he loosed the prisoner's bonds and took the stone from off his neck. He proved to be a stalwart baron, Arthur's friend, who thanked Sir Gareth gratefully and prayed him to ride back unto his castle that he might there reward him for his deed.

"Sir," said Sir Gareth sharply, "I will have no reward. For the deed's sake only did I do the deed."

And with his lady he rode on again. But Lynette bespake him all as haughtily as before. "Scullion, think not that I accept thee aught the more for running down these craven fellows with thy spit! A thresher with his flail had scattered them as easily. Nay, for thou smellest of the kitchen still."

Sir Gareth only answered, "Say thy say, and I will do my deed!"

Thus they rode on, and ever the lady chid him as before. That night they rested in the wood and on the morrow rose and brake their fast, then took their horses and rode on their way. The sun was scarcely risen above the tree-tops when at length they reached the first pass of the stream that coiled about the castle. Beyond a bridge that spanned the river with a single arch there rose a silk pavilion, yellow in hue with yellow banner flying, and before it paced a knight of huge, gigantic mould in yellow armor. When the Yellow Knight espied the damsel he cried out, "Ho, Damsel, hast thou brought this knight from Arthur's court to be thy champion?"

"Nay! nay, Sir Knight," Lynette quoth shrilly, "this is but a kitchen knave sent by King Arthur in much scorn of thee!" And turning to Sir Gareth she said, "Sir Scullion, flee now while thou mayest. For here stands one thou wilt not dare to face. Flee down the valley ere he gets to horse and none will cry thee shame. For thou art not knight but knave!"

Said Gareth, "Damsel, I had liefer fight a score of knights than bear the stinging wounds of words like thine!"

Then cried the Yellow Knight, "A kitchen knave and sent in scorn of me! With such I will not deign to fight! I will but hurl him from his horse then take his steed and arms, and so return him to his cursed King!"

"Dog!" cried Sir Gareth, " 'twere well to win my horse and arms ere making thus much talk of taking them!"

He spake and all at fiery speed the two shocked on the bridge. Their spears both bent but did not break and both knights shot from out their saddles to the ground. Full quickly they arose and drew their swords and Gareth lashed so fiercely with his brand he drave his enemy backward down the bridge, whereat the damsel cried, "Well stricken, kitchen-knave!" So fought they till Sir Gareth laid his enemy grovelling on the ground. Then cried the fallen, "Take not my life! I yield!" And Gareth said, "So this damsel ask it of me, good!—then will I spare thy life."

"Insolent scullion!" cried Lynette, and all her face flushed rosy red. "I ask of thee? I will be bound for nothing unto thee!"

"Then shall he die!" And Gareth there unlaced his helmet as to slay him, but she shrilled, "Be not so hard, Sir Scullion!"

"Damsel," Sir Gareth said, "thy charge to me is pleasure. At thy command his life is spared. Arise, Sir Knight, and pass to Arthur's hall! See that thou crave his pardon for thy crimes. Thy shield is mine! Farewell! And, damsel, lead and I follow!"

Fast away she fled. "Methought but now," she cried, "when I watched thee striking on the bridge, the savor of thy kitchen came upon me a little faintlier, but the wind hath changed. I scent it twenty fold!"

Sir Gareth answered laughingly. "The knave that doth thee full service of a knight is all as good, meseems, as any knight toward freeing of thy sister!"

"Sir Knave," she cried, "thou art peacocked up with thy

success! But at this next turning thou wilt meet thy match!"

So when they reached the second river loop, they saw across a shallow ford a second huge knight all in green armor. Beholding with Lynette one bearing his brother's shield, he cried, "Is that my brother there with thee?"

"Nay!" piped Lynette, "this is but a kitchen knave that hath overthrown thy brother and taken his arms."

"False traitor!" bawled the Green Knight, "thou shalt die!"

Therewith he blew a blast upon a horn all green. There came three damsels from a green pavilion and armed him with a shield and spear, both green. Astride a monstrous horse he rushed upon Sir Gareth. In midstream they met. At the first shock they brake their spears, and then they drew their swords and each gave other battle. A long while they fought thus, but at the last Sir Gareth smote the Green Knight such a buffet on the helm, that he fell heavily on his knees and yielded him. "O pray thee, slay me not, Sir Knight!" he begged. And so Sir Gareth sent him likewise to the King. Once more he cried unto Lynette, "Lead and I follow!" Quietly she led.

Said Gareth, "Hath the wind not changed again?"

"Nay, not a point! Right soon thou shalt be overcome!"

So they rode on and by mid-afternoon came to the last loop of the river. Here on a grassy plain there rose a silk pavilion all blood red, and round about on dark and mournful elms were hanging by the neck nigh forty goodly knights,—a woful sight!

"These knights," the damsel said, "came hither to do battle for my sister. All these the Red Knight overcame and put to such a shameful death. In the same wise will he serve thee!"

"A shameful knight who useth shameful customs," Gareth cried. "I fear him not!"

And then they saw fast by the stream a sycamore tree and thereon hung an horn, the greatest that ever they saw, made all of an elephant's bone. Thereunto Sir Gareth spurred his horse

and blew the horn so eagerly that all the forest rang. The Red Knight issued forth completely armed—a huge and threatening figure looming up in sinister blood red.

"Beware, Sir Fool," he roared. "Hath not the sight of yonder knights taught thee thou shouldst beware?"

"Weenest thou that such a shameful sight should make me fear? Nay, truly, it but causes me to have more hardihood to meet with thee!"

And so the two knights shocked together on the bridge. Both fell from off their horses and addressed themselves to battle on foot. A fearful struggle followed, for this knight had thrice the strength and fierceness of the other two. Like boars they fought. They hewed great pieces from their harness and their shields. Oft Gareth brought the Red Knight to his knees, but ever he vaulted up again and smote the harder, till Sir Gareth panted with the long-drawn struggle. But now Lynette called out, "Well done, knave-knight! Well stricken, knight-knave! O knave as noble as any knight, strike! thou art worthy of the Table Round! Strike! Strike! The wind will never change again!"

When Sir Gareth heard her speaking thus, he doubled his pace, and smote his foe so thick he drave him to the bridge's edge, and there at last forced that foul slayer of men to lose his footing, so he fell headlong to the stream. And then Sir Gareth cried again unto Lynette, "Lead and I follow!" But the damsel full gently said, "I lead no longer. Ride thou at my side. Thou art the kingliest of kitchen knaves! Shamed am I that I so reviled thee. But I am noble and did think the King had scorned me to give me but a kitchen knave, and now thy pardon, friend, for thou art wholly brave yet ever courteous and gentle withal."

"Damsel, thou art not all to blame," Sir Gareth said. "I should have small esteem for any knight who let a maiden's words arouse his anger!"

Then cried the damsel, "Now thou hast done enough! Wonders thou hast done. Miracles thou canst not! Turn back and fetch Sir Lancelot to meet this last gigantic knave. I dare not have thee face this hideous man-monster who guards my sister's castle. So terrible is he that he never shows his face by day. But I have watched him like a phantom glide about at night. Nor have I ever heard his voice. Always he hath made a mouthpiece of his page who still reported him as having in himself the strength of ten. He calleth himself Death! O I beg thee face him not!"

But Gareth only went more straightly forward. Thus they came in gloomy twilight dusk upon the castle and there before it rose a huge pavilion all in black beside which hung a long black horn. Sir Gareth grasped the horn and blew a mighty blast. Within the palace lights began to twinkle, and high up in the tower, at one bright window Lady Lyonors appeared. Below came sound of muffled voices through the gloom, and hollow tramplings up and down while weird, misshapen shadows flitted past. Three times Sir Gareth blew his eager blast. Then through the black pavilion's gloomy folds, high on a coal-black steed there issued slowly forth the monster-knight in coal-black arms, whereon in white a ghastly skeleton gleamed and on his helm a grinning skull. In the half light he came advancing but he spake no word. Thereat in indignation Gareth called, "Fool! Canst

thou not trust the strength thy God hath given thee, but to make
the terror of thee more, must trick thyself out thus?"

Still the monster spake no word which made the horror of
him all the more. His black horse bounded forward. Sir Gareth
met him with a steady shock. Then lo! what wonder came to
pass! He of that fearful aspect, fell at the first encounter easily
to ground. He rose and with one stroke Sir Gareth clove the
grinning skull and helmet underneath. And out from all that
trickery of terror issued but the bright face of a blooming boy.

"O Knight!" he cried. "Slay me not! My brothers bade
me do it to make a horror all about the place! They never dreamed
their passes would be passed."

Thus was the Lady Lyonors set free and in the castle was high
revel held that eventide, that after all their foolish fears he whom
they had so dreaded, was proven but a blooming boy. And in
good time, some say, Sir Gareth won Lynette to be his bride.

OPPORTUNITY*

Edward Rowland Sill

This I beheld, or dreamed it in a dream:
There spread a cloud of dust along a plain,
And underneath the cloud, or in it, raged
A furious battle, and men yelled, and swords
Shocked upon swords and shields.   A prince's banner
Wavered, then staggered backward, hemmed by foes.

A craven hung along the battle's edge,
And thought: "Had I a sword of keener steel—
That blue blade that the king's son bears,—but this
Blunt thing!" He snapped and flung it from his hand,
And lowering crept away and left the field.

Then came the king's son, wounded, sore bestead,
And weaponless, and saw the broken sword,
Hilt buried in the dry and trodden sand,
And ran and snatched it, and with battle shout
Lifted afresh, he hewed his enemy down,
And saved a great cause on that heroic day.

*Used by permission of Houghton Mifflin Company.

18

FROM THE TOWER WINDOW

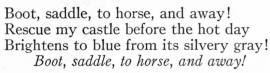

A CAVALIER TUNE
Boot and Saddle
ROBERT BROWNING

Boot, saddle, to horse, and away!
Rescue my castle before the hot day
Brightens to blue from its silvery gray!
Boot, saddle, to horse, and away!

Ride past the suburbs, asleep as you'd say;
Many's the friend there, will listen and pray
"God's luck to gallants that strike up the lay—
Boot, saddle, to horse, and away!"

Forty miles off, like a roebuck at bay,
Flouts Castle Brancepeth the Roundheads array!
Who laughs, "Good fellows ere this, by my fay,
Boot, saddle, to horse, and away!"

Who? My wife Gertrude; that, honest and gay,
Laughs when you talk of surrendering, "Nay!
I've better counsellors; what counsel they?
Boot, saddle, to horse, and away!"

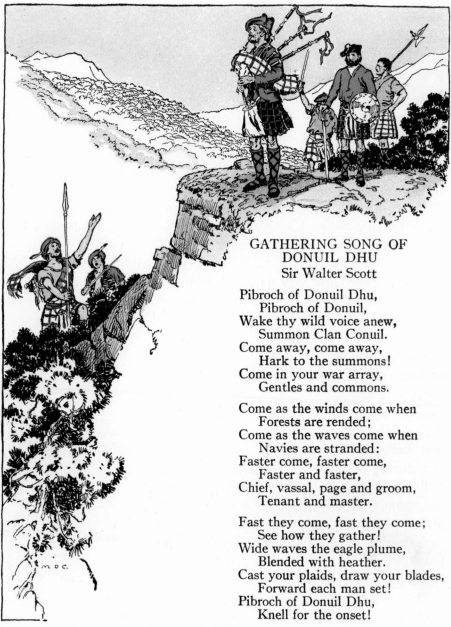

GATHERING SONG OF DONUIL DHU
Sir Walter Scott

Pibroch of Donuil Dhu,
　　Pibroch of Donuil,
Wake thy wild voice anew,
　　Summon Clan Conuil.
Come away, come away,
　　Hark to the summons!
Come in your war array,
　　Gentles and commons.

Come as the winds come when
　　Forests are rended;
Come as the waves come when
　　Navies are stranded:
Faster come, faster come,
　　Faster and faster,
Chief, vassal, page and groom,
　　Tenant and master.

Fast they come, fast they come;
　　See how they gather!
Wide waves the eagle plume,
　　Blended with heather.
Cast your plaids, draw your blades,
　　Forward each man set!
Pibroch of Donuil Dhu,
　　Knell for the onset!

FROM THE TOWER WINDOW

Robert Bruce, Scotland's Hero

AMONG the wild highlands of Scotland, by her plunging mountain torrents, and emerald mountain lakes, have always dwelt a people sturdy and independent, staunchly upholding their liberties with a spirit as keen and vigorous as the breath of their mountain air.

In the thirteenth century, King Edward I of England, better known as Edward Longshanks from the prodigious length of his legs, possessed himself by force and cunning of the Kingdom of Scotland and governed it with tyranny. For some twenty years the Scottish people suffered all manner of injustice, all manner of insults and injuries, and their great leader, William Wallace, was hanged on Tyburn Hill. Then awoke in the heart of one loyal Scotsman, Robert Bruce, a descendant of the ancient line of Scottish kings, the determination to rise up against the English, claim the throne of Scotland, and lead his down-trodden countrymen to battle for their freedom.

Galloping to the border, a hero determined to fight though he had not a sign of an army, he met Sir John, the Red Comyn, a strong and forceful baron, who had been his rival for the throne. Eagerly he desired to persuade the Red Comyn to join him, that they might by their common efforts expel the foreign foe. They met before the high altar of an ancient church in Dumfries, but during the course of their talk, they suddenly fell to quarrelling, ripping out abusive words. Then Bruce, by nature courteous, generous and wise, lost all control of himself, and in a moment of fury, struck Comyn down with his dagger. Having done this rash deed, he instantly took to his horse and fled. So had he begun his great work of freeing Scotland! So had he let his wild passions build up an obstacle for him at the outset of his career!

How desperate he was now and how consumed with remorse! To have set out to free his country and to have begun by clouding

Scotch folk music, such as *The Campbells Are Coming* and *My Heart's in the Highlands*, reflects love of home and country and sturdy independence. The national instrument is the bagpipe and the national dance, the highland fling.

his soul with such a crime as this! He had cut off from his cause all the followers of the Red Comyn when Scotland had such need of unity and the support of all her sons! Endless were his regrets; but he could not undo his crime.

Hastily he summoned to meet him those few barons who still had hopes for the freedom of Scotland and in the Abbey of Scone where the kings of Scotland always assumed their authority, he had himself hastily crowned in March, 1306. The rich light from the stained-glass windows streamed down on a slender gathering for such an affair of state, and everything relating to the ceremony was performed with the utmost haste. Longshanks had carried off to England the ancient crown of Scotland and a small circle of gold was hurriedly made to take its place. The Earl of Fife, whose duty it was to have placed the crown on the head of the King, refused to attend the rude ceremony; but his sister, the Countess of Buchan, not waiting for his consent, and officiating in his stead, crowned Robert Bruce as king.

Edward was greatly incensed when he heard what had taken place and he set out at once for Scotland at the head of a powerful army. Bruce met many defeats until he was driven with his wife, the faithful Countess of Buchan, and a few other loyal followers including young James of Douglas, to seek refuge in the mountains. Here in the hidden valleys and lonely tangled recesses of the heather-covered hills, they were chased from place to place, half-starving and in great danger. Everywhere Bruce found enemies. Sometimes they attacked him openly, sometimes with the slyest stealth. It took a stout heart in those days for Bruce to cling to his purpose and never give up his hope that he should set Scotland free. On the beautiful shores of Loch Lomond, girt by wild green mountains, amid the majestic grandeur of nature's most royal halls, Bruce and his Queen held court with a band of ragged followers. The men hunted deer in the forest and fished in the rocky streams, while the Queen and her ladies cooked and watched the pots over the camp-fire like the meanest of kitchen knaves. At last as winter drew near with the hint of snow in the air, living in such a rude fashion became too hard for the ladies. Bruce had to leave his wife in his only remaining castle, Kildrummie in Aberdeenshire, where he placed her under the care of his handsome young brother, Nigel, while he himself went off to seek a winter refuge on the lonely island of Rachrin off the Irish coast.

But scarcely were the women established, when the English came marching down and took Kildrummie Castle. They put the brave and beautiful youth, Nigel Bruce, to death, and threw the women into strict confinement, treating them with the utmost severity. The Countess of Buchan, who had greatly offended Edward by placing the crown on the head of Bruce, was imprisoned in an iron cage in the castle of Berwick as though she had been a wild beast.

News of the taking of Kildrummie, the captivity of his wife and the execution of Nigel reached Bruce in his miserable cabin at Rachrin and reduced him almost to despair. His crime in the church at Dumfries still weighed heavily on his soul and as he lay one morning on his wretched bed, he began to debate whether he had not better resign all thoughts of attempting again to make good his claim to the throne of Scotland and, instead, redeem his great sin by going to the Holy Land to fight against the foes of Christianity. But then it seemed both criminal and cowardly to give up his attempts to restore freedom to Scotland while there yet remained the smallest chance of success. As he lay there, divided betwixt these two courses of action, his eye was suddenly attracted by a spider which was hanging at the end of a long thread from one of the beams above him and endeavoring to swing itself to another beam for the purpose of fixing the line on which it meant to stretch its web. The insect made the attempt again and again without success. Six times Bruce counted that it tried to carry its point and failed, and it came into his head that he had fought just six battles against the English, and that the poor persevering spider was in exactly the same situation as himself, having made as many trials and been as often disappointed.

"Now," thought Bruce, "I will be guided by this spider. If the insect shall make another effort to fix its thread and be successful, I will venture a seventh time to try my fortunes in Scotland, but if it shall fail, I will give up hope and go to the Holy Land."

At that the spider swung itself again with all the force it could muster, and lo! the seventh time it succeeded! It fastened its thread to the distant beam! At once Bruce determined, notwithstanding the smallness of the means at his command, to set out for Scotland and persist in his first great plan.

On the mainland he was joined again by Douglas and others of his faithful followers, and they began to skirmish so successfully with the English as to force Lord Percy to retire from the province of Carrick. Bruce then dispersed his men upon various adventures against the enemy, but by thus doing, he left himself with such a small body of attendants that he often ran great risk of his life.

Once as he lay concealed in his own earldom of Carrick, certain men from the neighboring county of Galloway heard that Bruce was in hiding near, having no more than sixty men with him. So they resolved to attack him by surprise, and for this purpose got together two hundred men and two or three bloodhounds. Bruce who was always watchful and vigilant, had received information that this party intended to come on him suddenly and by night. Accordingly he quartered his little troop of sixty men on the side of a deep and swift-running river that had very steep rocky banks. There was but one ford by which this river could be crossed in that neighborhood, and that ford was so deep and narrow that two men could scarcely get through abreast. The ground on which they would land was steep and the path which led upwards from the water's edge was extremely narrow and difficult. Bruce caused his men to lie down to sleep at a place

about a half a mile distant from the river while he himself with
two attendants went down to watch the ford. As he stood by
the rushing river, he soon heard in the distance the baying of a
hound. At first he thought of going back to awaken his men, but
then he reflected that it might be only some shepherd's dog.

"My men," he said, "are sorely tired. I will not disturb
their sleep for the yelping of a cur till I know more of the matter."

Slowly the cry of the hound came nearer, then Bruce began
to hear a trampling of horses, the voices of men, and the ring and
clatter of armor.

"If I go back now to give my men the alarm," thought Bruce,
"those Galloway men will get through the ford without opposition,
and that would be a pity since it is so advantageous a place."

He therefore sent his followers to awaken his men and remained
altogether alone by the bank of the stream. The noise and the

trampling of horses increased and soon, emerging from the black shadows of the distant forest into the bright moonlight that streamed across the river, he saw two hundred men with gleaming arms. The men of Galloway on their part, beheld but a single figure looming beside the ford, and the foremost of the party plunged confidently into the water. But as they could pass the stream only one at a time, Bruce met them with his spear when they landed and in such stout fashion that none climbed the bank alive. Soon the Galloway men began to fall back in terror, but perceiving that it was only one man who had checked their two hundred, they plunged forward with furious rage to assault him. By this time, however, the King's soldiers had come hurrying to assist him, and the Galloway men at sight of them beat a hasty and inglorious retreat.

Many an adventure of the same type befell the Bruce, yet he began to win some small successes against the English and these successes gradually grew larger and more important, till one by one the great Scottish nobles seeing him doggedly persistent, unfailingly courageous, and wondrously wary and intelligent, began to give up their grudges against him and rally to his standard, thus placing at last beneath his command a large and powerful army. In all parts of Scotland deeds of daring were done to drive the English out of their strongholds and this not only by the Douglas and other great nobles but also by the stout yeomanry and bold peasants of the land, who were as anxious to possess their small cottages in honorable independence as the nobles to reclaim their castles. Everywhere throughout Scotland, the determination to fight for their liberties was at last, by one man's persistent effort, fired into living flame.

But now Edward Longshanks was dead and his son, Edward II, assembled one of the greatest armies which a king of England ever commanded, for the purpose of subduing Scotland. King Robert's army was scarcely a third as large and in matter of arms far more

FROM THE TOWER WINDOW

poorly provided. But during his eight long years of preparation for this great final test, King Robert had proved himself well able to make up by intelligent disposal of his troops what he lacked in arms and numbers. Moreover, his men had grown accustomed to fighting and gaining victories against every disadvantage.

Knowing that the superiority of the English lay in their splendid heavy armed cavalry and in their archers, which were better trained than any in the world, King Robert laid his plans carefully to overcome these odds. He led his army down into a plain near Stirling, where the English host must needs pass through a boggy country to reach them, while the Scots stood on hard, dry ground. He then caused all the ground on the front of his line where cavalry were likely to act to be dug full of holes about as deep as a man's knee. These were filled with brushwood, and the turf was replaced on the top so that no sign of them appeared.

When the Scottish army was drawn up, the line stretched on the south to the banks of the brook called Bannockburn, which are so rocky that no troops could attack them there, and on the north almost to the town of Stirling. Bruce reviewed his troops very carefully; all the useless servants, drivers of carts, and such he ordered to go behind a height, afterwards called in memory of the event, the Gillies' Hill, that is the servant's hill. He then made a stirring address to his soldiers, expressing his determination to gain the victory or lose his life on the field of battle and urging all who were not like-minded to leave ere the battle began.

Soon from the heights could be seen the approach of the vast English host, a beautiful and terrible sight, for the whole country seemed covered with men at arms on horse and foot, and above them waved a gallant show of standards, banners and pennons. As the van drew near, one among the English knights, Sir Henry de Bohun, saw King Robert, mounted not on his great war horse but on a little pony, riding up and down the ranks of his army, putting his men in order and carrying no spear, since he had no

27

thought that there would be fighting that evening. Thinking to take him unawares and so easily bear him to the ground, de Bohun galloped upon him. Robert saw the danger but stood perfectly still till de Bohun drew very near, then he suddenly swerved his pony just a little to one side. So Sir Henry missed him with his lance point and was in the act of being carried past him by the career of his horse when King Robert rose up in his stirrups and struck him a blow with his battle axe that hurled him lifeless from his saddle.

On the morrow, June 24, 1314, the battle began in earnest. The English archers started the fray by sending a hail of arrows into the Scottish ranks. But King Robert had in readiness a body of men-at-arms who rode at full gallop among the archers and as the latter had no weapons save their bows and arrows which they could not use when attacked hand to hand, they were cut down in great numbers by the Scottish horsemen and thrown into total confusion. The splendid English cavalry advanced at high speed to support the archers, but as they came dashing over the ground which was dug full of pits the horses fell into these holes, and the riders lay tumbling about without any means of defence, unable to rise from the weight of their armor. Then the English began to fall into general disorder and the Scottish king bringing up more forces, vigorously pressed his advantage. On a sudden while the battle was still obstinately maintained on both sides, the servants and attendants of the Scottish camp, seeing their masters were likely to gain the day, and wishing to share in the victory, ran forth from their conceal-ment behind the Gillies' Hill. Seeing them come suddenly over the ridge the English mistook the rabble for another army come to sustain the Scots, and losing all heart they broke ranks and fled.

Thus by the victory of Bannockburn, Robert Bruce, so long an exile, at last won the freedom of Scotland, and he is universally held to have been one of Scotland's strongest and wisest kings.

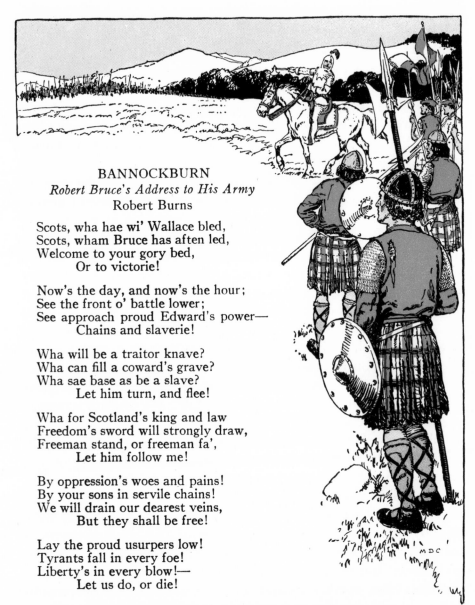

BANNOCKBURN
Robert Bruce's Address to His Army
Robert Burns

Scots, wha hae **wi'** Wallace bled,
Scots, wham Bruce has aften led,
Welcome to your gory bed,
    Or to victorie!

Now's the day, and now's the hour;
See the front o' battle lower;
See approach proud Edward's power—
    Chains and slaverie!

Wha will be a traitor knave?
Wha can fill a coward's grave?
Wha sae base as be a slave?
    Let him turn, and flee!

Wha for Scotland's king and law
Freedom's sword will strongly draw,
Freeman stand, or freeman fa',
    Let him follow me!

By oppression's woes and pains!
By your sons in servile chains!
We will drain our dearest veins,
    But they shall be free!

Lay the proud usurpers low!
Tyrants fall in every foe!
Liberty's in every blow!—
    Let us do, or die!

It is said that the patriotic hymn, *Scots Wha' Hae' Wi' Wallace Bled*, was first sung by Robert Bruce's army when they marched to Bannockburn, in 1314.

The Children's Crusade

IN THE year 1212, when the Saracens held the Holy Land, and
the greatest Christian warriors had been unable in four crusades
to win it back for Christianity, there dwelt in the village of Cloyes,
near Orleans, a shepherd lad named Stephen. Stephen knew little
of the world except the hillsides about his village, but boylike,
he loved stories and listened open-mouthed to the tales of pilgrims
and travelers who chanced to come through Cloyes. From them,
he learned all about what had happened in Palestine, how the
Saracens held possession of the sacred tomb of Christ, and no
Christian army seemed strong enough to redeem it out of their
hands.

One day Stephen went to the neighboring city of Chartres, and
there he saw a procession. A long line of black-clad priests carrying crosses draped in black, marched sadly through the streets,
singing doleful litanies, and imploring God's mercy on behalf of
those who had suffered in the Holy Land. Then Stephen knelt
with the crowd, and he felt his heart burn within him. With all
the ardor of youth, he longed to save Jerusalem.

For many days thereafter, as he tended his sheep on the hillsides, he thought and longed and dreamed, till his head was full
of fancies. Then behold, in his loneliness, Stephen saw a vision.
Stephen saw Jesus himself, bidding him gather the children of
Europe and lead them to the Holy Land. Awe-struck, the boy
rushed home to tell his mother his vision.

Soon, in great excitement, he was arguing with the villagers
who ridiculed his tale or said he had been asleep. But neither
the boy's own parents nor the wiseacres of the village could shake
his faith in his mission, and, seeing their disbelief, he left his home
and family to carry his story elsewhere.

Five miles north of Paris, lay the shrine of St. Denys, the
holiest shrine in France. Here was kept the *or'i-flamme*, the

sacred banner fashioned like a triple-tongued flame, which the kings of France carried into battle against the nation's foes; and here thousands of pilgrims came to seek help of the holy Saint, whose tomb was within the church.

Outside the door of the church, Stephen took his stand and, day after day, he preached. Day after day he made his appeal, a Crusade of the children of Europe to save the Holy Land! The tomb of the Christ-Child, he said, was in the hands of strangers! The little Christ was deserted, insulted, and abandoned to infidel Arabs and Turks. Children crowded around and hearkened with all their souls. Grown people listened also and marveled at the lad. Surely God must inspire him! An untaught peasant-lad to speak with such faith as this! Perhaps there was truth in his words. Were not men beginning to say that grown men were too wicked to save the Holy Sepulchre? Perhaps the children could do it—little lambs, so pure! Their hearts, at least were pure. Strong in the strength of their innocence, they might win, perchance prevail where grown men had failed.

Stephen knew that his message must be borne throughout all of France while enthusiasm ran high; so he bade the children, who heard him, each to return to his home and preach the Crusade to his friends. Back to their farms and villages the little disciples went and soon every part of France, every farthest valley, rang with the name of Stephen and the call to Palestine. And, from every corner of France, children responded to the call.

31

Fastening on their breasts the red Crusader's Cross, they put on the broad-brimmed pilgrim's hat, took up the pilgrim's staff, and, forming themselves into bands each with its own special leader, they marched through towns and villages seeking new recruits.

From castle and cottage by the wayside, children heard their call and ran to join the throng. The goose-girl left her geese; the herd-boy left his goats; and the baron's son, looking down from the height of his lofty tower, saw visions of prancing horses, armor, and streaming banners, with himself the bravest of knights. He, too, hastened down to join the swelling throng. The children all seemed bewitched. It was as if some magic piper had charmed

Songs which the Crusaders sang as they marched have been handed down to us. Among these songs are *Merci Clamant* by Chatelain de Coucy, a knight who went to the Holy Land with the soldiers of Richard, the Lion Hearted; and, the Crusader's Hymn.

FROM THE TOWER WINDOW

them to leave their homes and, with irresistible summons, had drawn them to follow him. Laughing and dancing along, they went merrily on their way as if they were bound for a picnic, all ignorant of the fate to which they were being lured. The children's parents were helpless. Nothing could shake their faith.

In vain did Philip Augustus issue a decree that the children must return to their homes. In vain did fathers and mothers lock up their children till the little ones sickened for longing. In vain did the wiser and kinder among the parish priests urge them to give up their plan. They would not listen to anyone, but shook off all restraint and, with dancing eyes, marched on.

The story of Stephen spread beyond the borders of France. A German lad, named Nicholas, gathered 20,000 children, who set out from Cologne, in June, 1212, waving green branches and singing hymns in the excess of their joy. It took longer for the children of France to gather at the city of Ven'dôme', for they came from a larger territory; but, by August, they, too, were assembled. The last bands arrived, and Stephen gave word to march. Thirty-thousand children marched out of the gates of Vendôme.

In front of the procession rode Stephen in a flower-decked wagon, sheltered beneath a canopy and sitting on a rich carpet, while around him rode a company of noble youths on horseback, bearing lances and spears. Stephen, the shepherd-boy, had now become Stephen, the prophet, the miracle-worker and saint! He must have a guard of honor and lead the procession in state!

Behind came the young Crusaders: boys, girls, and even babies wearing on breast or shoulder the red cross which was their pride. In their hands they bore wooden crosses and little childish copies of the oriflamme of France, for were they not all warriors? Some carried candles as in the Saint's Day procession, and even the tiniest children who clung to their brothers and sisters waved a green branch in one hand. And one and all they

The legend of the *Pied Piper of Hamelin*, as told in Browning's poem, grew out of the fascination which the fanatical appeal of leaders of the Children's Crusade had for the children of France and Germany, so that they seemed charmed from their homes to follow Stephen and Nicholas.

shouted the old crusading cry: *"Dieu le volt!"* "God wills it!"

As the good folk of Vendôme watched them troupe by in an endless stream, it seemed that the life-blood of France was slowly ebbing past.

Day after day the children journeyed, singing, toward the sea, for they knew that the sea lay between them and Jerusalem. When they halted in the heat of noonday, Stephen preached a sermon from his wagon, and again he preached at night when they camped in the fields by the roadside. To his excited followers, Stephen seemed a god! "They vied in efforts to procure from his person or chariot some little fragment, which was kept as a relic and valued as a charm. They, who had succeeded in securing a thread of his raiment or a piece of the trappings of the car or even of the accoutrements of the horses, showed them with exultation to the others; while they who had a single hair of his head were regarded as possessors of a priceless treasure."

At first, the way was easy and led through smiling fields and friendly villages; but later, there came bare heaths parched by the sun. Here, there was nothing to eat save a few poor roots and berries, and the tired and footsore children toiled wearily in the heat. Even the brooks were dry, and little throats grew parched so that the brave songs died and the joyous shouts were stilled.

Some of the weaker children turned back to their homes; and some, who lay down at night after the weary day's journey, never woke again. Others left the trail and fell a prey to wild beasts or to still wilder brigands. But the main army marched on with most incredible faith; and, each time they caught sight of the turrets of a castle or the roofs of some distant village, the smallest one would ask, "Is that Jerusalem?"

At last they climbed the last hill. They looked down on the blue sea and saw the coast city of Marseilles spread out at their feet. Somewhere across that water lay the Holy Land, and Stephen had said that God would divide the waters for them

FROM THE TOWER WINDOW

just as He once divided the waters of the Red Sea, that His pilgrims might cross dry shod. Down to the city gates ran the little Crusaders and begged to be admitted.

The good people of Marseilles had seen many a crusading army, but never such an one as this. They looked at the eager young faces. They heard the excited shouts, "Tomorrow God will open us a passage through the sea! Tomorrow we shall see Jerusalem!" But the good people of Marseilles sadly shook their heads. They had lived by the sea too long to believe in any miraculous parting of the waves.

That night the children slept in friendly houses or churches, or even in the streets; but, at daybreak, they crowded to the water's edge and waited breathlessly for the promised path to appear.

Monotonously the waves rose and fell again; rose and fell again in undisturbed, age-old rhythm; and, as far as the eye could see, the sunshine sparkled on the water. The hearts of the children fell. Stephen, too, seemed bewildered. All day long they waited,

but the waters did not divide; and, at night, they turned sadly away from the sea and wandered back to the town.

But no long time had elapsed ere two owners of gallant ships, Hugo Ferreus and William Porcus, offered to carry to Palestine as many of these small Crusaders as really cared to go. This, they said, they would do "for the cause of God and without any price!" The children were wild with joy! This was the passage through the waters! This was God's way of bringing his chosen warriors to Jerusalem!

Seven ships were made ready, and, when the day of sailing came, five-thousand eager children, with a sprinkling of priests and pilgrims, were carried aboard in skiffs. The children were off at last; and from "castles" and crowded decks, there rose the sound of singing as the deep voices of the priests and the high, sweet treble of the children joined in the old crusading hymn, *Veni, Creator Spiritus.* In a trice the wind filled the sails and, with streamers and oriflammes fluttering gaily at their mastheads, the seven vessels danced over the deep blue waves till they disappeared from sight.

For eighteen long years no word came back to Marseilles of either vessels or children. They had disappeared as if by magic.

At last, there came an old man who told a tragic tale. He had been a priest on board one of those miserable vessels. In a hideous storm at sea, he had seen two ships dashed to pieces on the rocks of the Isle of Falcons and every soul on board lost; but after all, these lost ones had met the happier fate. He had seen the five other ships weather the storm and sail on, sail on not to the Holy Land, but to the awful slave-markets of the pitiless, sinister East.

For the kindly-seeming merchants were the cruelest of cruel slave-dealers, heartless and greedy. They sold the children to the Arabs, and, instead of marching triumphantly into a new-won Jerusalem, the little Crusaders languished in many a Moslem household from Algiers as far as Bagdad.

The only ones who ever saw the Jerusalem of their dream, saw it as they marched in chains to the homes of their Moslem masters. Not one of five-thousand children, who set out from Marseilles, ever returned to the homes they had so eagerly left behind them.

Nor did the German children, whom Nicholas had led, meet a much happier fate. Many fell to the robber-barons who lived in the turreted castles along the banks of the Rhine. More were devoured by the fierce wild beasts in the forests of the Rhine-land. Only seven thousand, cold and pinched with hunger, survived the bitter snows and dangerous roads of the Alps; and these, coming down into Italy, were refused ships by the Genoese and ordered home by the Pope.

Not more than a ragged handful ever came back again; but, in hundreds of castles and cottages throughout France and Germany, old people sat in their empty rooms, remembering the children's voices that had echoed there so merrily, and the children's feet that had danced there so happily in the long, long ago.

The Song of Roland

A French Epic, retold from the Chanson de Roland

FOR seven years Emperor Charlemagne* fought Saracens in Spain. All the land had he conquered from the highlands to the sea. Before the might of his arms, castle and keep went down; no city could withstand him save only Sar'a-gos'sa, the strong walled mountain town. Helpless in Saragossa, Mar-sile', the Saracen chief, bewailed his fate to come, till crafty counsellors, plotting, came whispering in his ear: "Send gifts to Charlemagne! Send lions, bears, and steeds! Send silver and rich gold. Say that thou seekest peace and promise at St. Mi'chael's feast to visit the Great King, and then to be baptized. Thereat he will depart and we will break our oath, rise up, and win back Spain!"

Marsile rejoiced to hear such words of trickery. He sent ambassadors with gifts to Cordova, and these found Charlemagne within a blossoming orchard's shade, there seated on a golden throne, imperial in majesty, with flowing beard and robes. Around him stood his peers to watch the martial games of fifty thousand warriors. Then unto Charlemagne the Saracens most humbly offered peace. But up spake Roland, sister's son to Charlemagne, the bravest and best-loved of all the King's young knights. "Marsile hath tricked us once. Why trust his promises again?"

Now Gan'e-lon, step-father to that splendid youth, stood by, dark-browed and evil, jealous hatred gnawing at his heart. "Rash fool!" he cried. "Thou arguest for war because thou prizest thine own glory more than all the lives of these, thy fellows here!" Whereat the King cried out: "Enough! We will accept the offer of Marsile!"

Then Roland and his comrade Oliver, besought the dangerous task of bearing back his answer to Marsile. But Charlemagne refused and bade them name some other in their stead. Quoth Roland: "Ganelon was anxious for the peace! Why not send Ganelon?"

*The *Lament for Charlemagne*, doubtless written in a monastery, was chanted in France and Germany, both of which countries he ruled. Charlemagne (742-814), did much to spread learning and was interested in the development of music.

FROM THE TOWER WINDOW

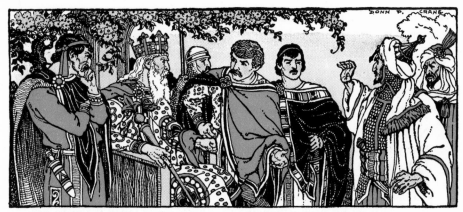

With inward fury Ganelon now heard these words and secretly vowed vengeance on the youth; for well he knew the expedition to Marsile would be so dangerous, that he who went, might nevermore return. But Charlemagne, in his imperial dignity, delivered unto Ganelon his glove as emblem of the office he bestowed, entrusting to his care the message to Marsile. Both rage and fear made Ganelon unsteady as he took the glove, so that he let it fall. Then great dismay came over all. "That bodeth little good," men said. And red with wrath, dark Ganelon departed with two Moors.

"While Roland lives, will fighting never cease!" he cried.

"But we could rid thee of him!" said the Moors; "Do thou but see that he commands the rear guard when thy great King Charlemagne departs at length from Spain!"

And so they planned to slay young Roland, and the chief, Marsile, gave Ganelon rich gifts and sent him safely home. And Ganelon delivered unto Charlemagne the keys of Saragossa, reporting that the infidels submitted to his will. Then Charlemagne thanked God and made all ready to depart for home.

"Who asks to lead my rear guard?" cried the King.

"Ah, who so brave as Roland?" Ganelon replied.

But Charlemagne made answer with some heat, "Nay! Roland shall remain with me!" Then Roland did himself so earnestly entreat to be entrusted with the dangerous post, that Charlemagne at last, though most reluctantly, gave his consent. Yet on the night before he left, his rest was troubled with strange dreams, through which the face of Ganelon passed ominous and dark. Foreboding ill, he bade young Roland sad farewell, and bade him, should the need arise, call aid with Ol'i-phant, his horn.

> Now Roland the Count hath ascended to the top of a barrow green
> Arrayed in the mail of his hauberk—better hath no man seen!
> Laced on his head is his helmet; right well it becometh a knight!
> No weapon forged may cleave it, how starkly soe'er one smite.
> To his side is Durendal girded, the golden-hilted sword!
> A shield from his neck is hanging that hath never failed its lord.
> A spear on high hath he lifted with fluttering pennon white;
> Low as his wrist are swinging the golden fringes bright;
> In his armour arrayed he seemeth a passing goodly knight!

With 20,000 brave men, with Oliver, his friend, dearer than any brother, with Turpin, the doughty Archbishop, who thought it no shame to tuck up his robes and strike a blow for Christ, Roland now waved farewell to the vanguard filing past in the narrow gorges below. "Farewell till we meet in France!"

With Ganelon in their midst, the vanguard marched toward home; but a nameless sense of evil haunted the souls of all, and their hearts were back with Roland on the treacherous soil of Spain.

> High were the peaks and the valleys deep,
> The mountains wondrous dark and steep;
> Sadly the Franks through the passes wound;
> Fully fifteen leagues did their tread resound.
> To their own great land they were drawing nigh,
> And they look on the fields of Gascony.
> They think of their homes and manors there,
> Their gentle spouses and damsels fair.
> Is none but for pity the tear lets fall,
> But the anguish of Karl is beyond them all.
> His sister's son at the gates of Spain
> Smites on his heart and he weeps amain.

FROM THE TOWER WINDOW

Early the following morning, the rear guard gaily advanced, young Roland and his friend Oliver riding blithely side by side. In joyous converse they passed out of the glistening sunlight into the darkness and gloom of the Pass of Ron'ces. Then suddenly Oliver reined in his horse, and shaded his face with his hand. "Behold!" he cried, hoarse with feeling, "the work of Ganelon!"

> To a high knoll Oliver spurreth; to the right he looked therefrom;
> Up the long green valley, he seeth the Saracens come . . .
> Helmets begemmed are flashing, shields blaze against the sun,
> The mail-coats glint through the surcoats with broidery overdone:
> Surges on surges of war-waves!—their numbers baffle the sight!
> Yea, Oliver's spirit is 'wildered, that he may not count them aright.
> Down from the crest of the barrow, full swiftly hath he spurred;
> He hath come to the Frankish heroes, bearing an evil word.

"Now shall we have grim battle," Roland cried to his men. And his warriors answered boldly: "A curse on him who flees!" But Oliver, seeing the foe outnumber them five to one, begged Roland to blow one good blast on Oliphant, his horn.

> Sound Oliphant, Roland my comrade, and straightway shall Charlemagne hear;
> He is threading the mountain gorges! Still, O still is he near.
> "Now God forbid," cried Roland, "that for any heathen born
> It shall ever be said that Roland hath stooped to sound his horn!
> Shall I be on the lips of my kinsmen, a byword, a shame and a scorn?"

Thrice Oliver well besought Roland, and thrice Roland answered: "Nay!" Then good Archbishop Turpin bade the Franks kneel in prayer and prepare their hearts for the battle.

> Now waxeth the battle wondrous, and its travail passing sore;
> Well Oliver and Roland the burden of that day bore;
> The Archbishop too, he fighteth and a thousand sword-strokes ring;
> There are the twelve peers smiting, unflinching, unfaltering.

Marsile himself fighteth with Roland grim in battle-stroke, but Roland's good sword Durendal, woundeth him unto the death. Each man in that small Frankish host did wondrous deeds that day.

And now before force of the Moors, one by one, the heroes fall, till amidst a great heap of slain, Roland urgeth a handful to stand to their posts till the death. And the Saracens, fearing that handful, attack them but from a distance with arrow and deadly spear. Mortally wounded thus, Oliver calleth to Roland, and Roland, although half-blinded, fighteth his way to his side. Then each lays his head to the other, and so doth Oliver die. Left alone of the Frankish host, did Roland and Archbishop Turpin now fight shoulder to shoulder, till Turpin, too, sinks to the ground. Then Roland, laying his friend on the grass and slowly unlacing his helmet, at last blows one long mournful blast on Oliphant, his horn. All nature shuddered with terror; for over the sunny fields of France there broke a hideous storm. Across the heavens the thunder rolled, the livid lightning flashed, and earth was shaken with grief. Then far away Charlemagne heard the sound of Roland's horn. "Our Roland is in danger!"

"Nay! nay!" quoth Ganelon, "belike he is but hunting."

Again that mournful call came wailing far away.

FROM THE TOWER WINDOW

"Never would he call like that unless in direst peril!"

"Nay! nay! he but chases a hare!"

Yet still a third time came that blast so long now and despairing that none might mistake its meaning.

"Roland is in extremity!" Charlemagne cried in anguish and he bade his men turn about and let all the trumpets blare that Roland might know he was coming, coming with all the thunderbeat of thousands of marching men.

At sound of Charlemagne's trumpets the Saracens fled from the field, yet fleeing, they flung back missiles till Roland was nigh to death. Then slowly, with mighty effort, he collected from mountain and valley the bodies of his twelve peers and dragged them to Archbishop Turpin's feet, that they might receive one last blessing. While laying Oliver there, Roland swooned for grief, and Turpin, seizing his horn, painfully raised himself to fetch his friend some water from the brook that ran nearby. But in his act of mercy, Turpin, too, fell dead, and Roland came to his senses to find himself alone. Grasping his good sword Du'ren-dal' and Oliphant, his horn, he toiled to the top of a hill that he might look off to Spain and die with his face toward the foe. Then lifting his sword, he tried with all his strength to break it, but the steel showed never a dent. So he laid Durendal beneath him with Oliphant, his horn, that even in death he might guard them, and there on the height, he died, committing his soul to God.

Charlemagne reached the valley. Deathly stillness reigned over all. He called on his peers by name. Not one there was to answer. And on the height, with his face toward Spain, they found the hero Roland. Great was the grief of all. Charlemagne hotly gave chase to the fleeing Saracen host and defeated them in a great battle; then bearing the body of Roland, he sadly returned to France. Laden with chains, dark Ganelon was condemned to death as a traitor; but wherever men loved brave deeds, they sang of Roland the hero, who stood to his post till the death.

43

The Legend of William Tell*

MANY years ago the free and sturdy people who lived in the quaint little villages among the mountains of Switzerland were ground down beneath the heel of the emperor of Austria and governed by Austrian bailiffs with the greatest cruelty and oppression. The most devoted patriots of the four forest cantons of Switzerland met, therefore, and determined to rise up and strike for their freedom. One moonlight night of October, 1307, a little band of these faithful men met on the Rütli, a small plateau overlooking the gleaming waters of the beautiful Lake of Lucerne. Beneath the open sky and in sight of the glistening snow-capped peaks that loom up about the lake, the three leaders of that little band clasped hands, raised three fingers to heaven, and solemnly swore to shake off the yoke of Austria.

Among the patriots who took the oath upon Rütli was a young man named William Tell, who was noted far and wide for his skill with the cross-bow and arrows. Strong and sure-footed was Tell and he delighted in pursuing the chamois over almost inaccessible heights, or plucking the snowy flower of the edelweiss from the edge of some dangerous precipice. With his wife and two little sons Tell lived in a cozy chalet at Bürglen in the canton of Uri.

About this time it came to pass that Gessler, an Austrian bailiff, determined to ascertain by a clever device how many men in Uri were loyal to his master. He therefore set up a pole in the quaint old market place of the village of Altdorf. On this pole he hung a hat—the emblem of Austrian power—and he bade a herald proclaim that all who passed must do homage to that hat under penalty of death or life-long imprisonment. The freemen of Uri were justly incensed when they heard this decree and by common consent avoided passing through the square. Those who must go that way made use of every possible excuse to avoid bending their heads to the hat.

Now at this time Tell living in his quiet chalet at some distance

*William Tell is the hero of a famous play by the German poet and dramatist, Johann Schiller, 1759-1805.

FROM THE TOWER WINDOW

from Altdorf, was ignorant of all that had recently happened there. One day he came down to the village bearing his cross-bow over his shoulder and holding his little son by his hand. Unconscious alike of pole, hat and guards he strolled across the square and was greatly surprised when suddenly a throng of soldiers surrounded him and placed him under arrest, crying out that he had defied the orders of Gessler. While Tell was protesting his innocence and striving to make the guards release him, he saw Gessler himself approaching on horseback around one of the quaintly painted houses that bordered on the square. Going at once to the bailiff, Tell loudly demanded justice. In the midst of a gathering crowd, the bailiff listened, sneering.

It happened, however, that Gessler had often heard men praise the remarkable skill of Tell as a marksman and he had long desired to see how well the man could shoot. Moreover, he wished to punish Tell in as cruel a way as he could devise, for his neglect of the hat in order to make him an example to the other rebellious inhabitants of Altdorf. Therefore he thundered forth: "You shall be free on one condition only—if you shoot an apple from the head of your son at a distance of one hundred and fifty paces!"

The people who stood about gasped, and a murmur of indignation went up from all the crowd, but so great was the fear that Gessler had inspired in them all that no one dared interfere. Tell himself, a moment before so confident and self possessed, seemed suddenly to collapse at hearing the bailiff's words. Gessler could have thought of nothing more cruel than thus to insist that the father must shoot at his own little son.

"Place any other punishment upon me!" cried Tell. "What if the boy should move? What if my hand should tremble?"

"Say no more!" cried Gessler. "Shoot!"

Tell was in despair, but the little lad, his face bright with perfect trust, ran and stood against a linden tree at one end of the square.

"Shoot, father!" he cried. "Shoot! I know you can hit the apple!"

The Overture from the Opera, *William Tell*, by the Italian Rossini, gives a beautiful picture of Alpine life—mountain sunrise, a storm, then calm and the herdsman's song, with the sound of shepherd's horns and cowbells.

The boy's absolute and fearless confidence determined Tell. Yet he still trembled as he selected two arrows from his quiver, while a soldier took an apple from a fruit vendor who stood near and placed it on the boy's head. One arrow Tell thrust hastily into his belt, the other he carefully adjusted in his cross-bow. For a moment his eyes followed the distant line of the snow-capped mountains, resting to gather strength on their calm and quiet peaks. Then his hand grew steady and he took aim.

Twang! went the bow. The arrow whistled through the air. All noise in the square was stilled and everyone held his breath. But lo! the arrow struck the apple squarely in the center, split it, and carried it away! The boy had not moved a hairsbreadth! A mighty shout went up from the crowd! But as Tell was turning away, Gessler pointed to the second arrow which the marksman had stuck in his belt.

"Fellow," cried he, "what did you mean to do with that arrow?"

"Tyrant," was Tell's proud answer, "that second arrow was for you if I had struck my child."

Beside himself with rage at these bold words, Gessler angrily bade his guards to bind Tell fast and convey him down to his waiting boat at Flühlen, whence he should be carried across the lake and cast into the foulest of dungeons. Friends led the little boy away, but in the train of the tyrant, Tell was marched in chains down to the edge of the Lake of Lucerne. Placed in the boat with fast bound hands and feet, his useless weapons beside him, Tell despairingly watched the bailiff embark and the shore near Altdorf slowly recede. Soon, however, clouds began to hide the sun and roll down over the pure white peaks. The ripples in the water grew into waves, the sky grew darker and darker. At last there broke a mighty storm on the little boat. Thunder crashed, the water heaved and dashed in angry foam and lightning streaked from shore to shore. In vain did the Austrians try to guide the boat through the tempest. They were not well enough acquainted

FROM THE TOWER WINDOW

with the lake. Then the boatsmen, knowing well that Tell was the most clever steersman in the canton of Uri, began to implore Gessler to let him be unbound in order to help them. In a voice that could scarcely be heard above the shriek of the storm, Gessler cried: "Unloose the prisoner's chains. Let him take the helm!"

Accordingly, Tell was unbound. He seized the helm and the boat went plunging forward. With a strong arm and fearless gaze he directed it straight toward a narrow ledge of rock which forms a natural landing place in the mighty cliffs that at this point rise up sheer from the lake. The water there is seven hundred feet deep, but as the boat drew near and a sudden flash of lightning revealed the spot, Tell suddenly let go of the rudder and with one mighty leap sprang from the pitching boat across the seething waves to the shore. There were angry cries from the lake, but Gessler's boat went drifting off into the darkness again, hurled back, wildly tossing among the waves.

Tell made his way straight around the lake to a spot that Gessler would have to pass on his way home after his landing. There, crouching in the bushes on the steep bank, he waited patiently to see whether the tyrant would escape the storm. At length the bailiff appeared, riding proudly at the head of his troops. Then Tell took his second arrow, the arrow that he had meant should wipe out tyranny from Switzerland. As Gessler passed by, he let the arrow fly, and true to its mark it sped. Gessler fell and with him Austria's reign of tyranny. For the Swiss people, encouraged at hearing what Tell had done, threw off the fear that had bound them, rose up and made Switzerland once more free.

Joseph and His Brethren

NOW Jacob loved Joseph more than all his children, because he was the son of his old age, and he made Joseph a coat of many colours. And when his brethren saw that their father loved Joseph best, they hated him and could not speak peaceably unto him. And his brethren went to feed his father's flock in Shechem. And Jacob said unto Joseph, "Go, I pray thee, and see whether it be well with thy brethren." And when Joseph's brethren saw him afar off, even before he came near, they conspired against him to slay him. But his brother Reuben said, "Let us not kill him, but cast him into this pit," for he intended secretly to save him.

And it came to pass when Joseph was come unto his brethren, that they stript Joseph of his coat and cast him into a pit. And they lifted up their eyes and behold, a company of Ishmaelites came from Gilead with their camels bearing spicery and balm and myrrh, to carry it down to Egypt. And they drew up Joseph out of the pit, and sold him to the Ishmaelites for twenty pieces of silver. And they took Joseph's coat, and killed a kid of the goats, and dipped the coat in the blood; and they brought the coat to their father, and said, "This have we found." And Jacob said, "It is my son's coat! An evil beast hath devoured him." And Jacob rent his clothes, and put sackcloth upon his loins, and mourned for his son many days.

And the Midianites sold Joseph into Egypt unto Pot'i-phar, the Captain of Pharaoh's guard. And when Joseph's master saw that the Lord was with him and made all that he did to prosper, he made him overseer over his house. But the wife of Potiphar hated Joseph and falsely accused him of crime, so that the wrath of Joseph's master was kindled and he put Joseph into prison.

FROM THE TOWER WINDOW

And it came to pass that the butler of the King of Egypt and his baker had offended their lord. And he put them in ward in the house where Joseph was bound. And they dreamed a dream both of them, and behold, they were sad. And they said unto Joseph, "We have dreamed a dream, and there is no interpreter of it."

And Joseph said unto them, "Do not interpretations belong to God? Tell me them, I pray you." And the chief butler told his dream to Joseph. And Joseph said unto him, "This is the interpretation of it: Yet within three days shall Pharaoh restore thee unto thy place: and thou shalt deliver Pharaoh's cup after the former manner into his hand. But when it shall be well with thee, I pray thee, make mention of me unto Pharaoh, for indeed I have done nothing that they should put me into the dungeon."

When the chief baker saw that the interpretation was good, he likewise told his dream unto Joseph. And Joseph answered and said, "This is the interpretation thereof: Yet within three days will Pharaoh lift up thine head from off thee, and shall hang thee on a tree." And it came to pass the third day, which was Pharaoh's birthday, that he made a feast unto all his servants. And he restored the chief butler unto his butlership again; but he hanged the chief baker as Joseph had interpreted to him. Yet did not the chief butler remember Joseph, but forgat him.

And it came to pass at the end of two full years, that Pharaoh dreamed and behold he stood by the river. And, behold, there came up out of the river seven well-favoured kine and fat-fleshed; and they fed in a meadow. And behold, seven other kine came up after them out of the river, ill-favoured and lean-fleshed; and stood by the other kine. And the ill-favoured and lean-fleshed kine did eat up the well-favoured and fat kine. So Pharaoh awoke.

And he slept and dreamed the second time. And it came to pass in the morning that his spirit was troubled; and he sent for all the magicians of Egypt, and all the wise men thereof, but there was none that could interpret the dreams unto Pharaoh.

Then spake the chief butler unto Pharaoh, saying: "Pharaoh was wroth with his servants, and put me in prison, both me and the chief baker: and we dreamed a dream in one night, I and he; and there was with us a young man, an Hebrew, and he interpreted to us our dreams. And it came to pass, as he interpreted to us."

Then Pharaoh sent and called Joseph, and they brought him hastily out of the dungeon: and he shaved himself, and changed his raiment, and came in unto Pharaoh. And Pharaoh said unto Joseph, "I have dreamed a dream, and there is none that can interpret it: and I have heard say of thee, that thou canst understand a dream to interpret it." And Joseph answered, saying, "It is not in me: God shall give Pharaoh an answer of peace."

And when Pharaoh had told Joseph his dream, Joseph said unto Pharaoh, "The seven good kine are seven years. Behold there come seven years of great plenty throughout all the land of Egypt: and the seven thin and ill-favoured kine that came up after them are seven years of famine, and the famine shall consume the land. Now, therefore, let Pharaoh look out a man discreet and wise, and set him over the land of Egypt. And let him appoint officers over the land, and let them gather all the food of those good years that come. And that food shall be as a store to the land against the seven years of famine."

And the thing was good in the eyes of Pharaoh. And Pharaoh said unto his servants, "Can we find such a one as this, a man in whom the spirit of God is?" And Pharaoh said unto Joseph, "For as much as God hath shewed thee all this, there is none so discreet and wise as thou art. Thou shalt be over my house."

And Pharaoh took off his ring from his hand, and put it on Joseph's hand, and arrayed him in vestures of fine linen, and put a gold chain about his neck; and he made him to ride in his second chariot which he had; and they cried before him, "Bow the knee," and he made him ruler over all the land of Egypt.

And in the seven plenteous years the earth brought forth by

FROM THE TOWER WINDOW

handfuls. And he laid up all the food in the cities. And seven years of dearth began to come, and the dearth was in all lands save Egypt. And all countries came unto Joseph to buy corn. And Jacob said to his sons: "Get you down and buy for us from thence." But Benjamin, his youngest son, Jacob sent not into Egypt, lest mischief should befall him; for Benjamin was a little one, a comfort to Jacob's heart, since his mother, Rachel, was dead and his brother, Joseph, was gone.

And Joseph's brethren came, and bowed before him with their faces to the earth. And Joseph knew his brethren, but made himself strange unto them, saying roughly: "Whence come ye?"

And they said, "From the land of Canaan to buy food."

And Joseph said unto them, "Ye are spies. Hereby ye shall be proved. If ye be true men, let one of your brethren be bound in the house of your prison. Go ye, carry corn for the famine of your houses, but bring your youngest brother unto me."

And they said one to another, "We are verily guilty concerning our brother, Joseph, and for that sin is this distress come upon us."

And they knew not that Joseph understood them; for he spake unto them by an interpreter. And he turned himself about from them and wept. Then he took from them Simeon, and bound him before their eyes and he commanded to fill their sacks with corn. And they laded their asses with the corn, and departed thence and told their father all that was come to pass. And their father Jacob said: "My son Benjamin shall not go down to Egypt!"

But the famine was sore in the land. And it came to pass that when they had eaten up the corn which they had brought out of

51

Egypt, their father said, "Go again, buy us a little food, take also your brother, and God Almighty give you mercy before the man."

And the men took a present and they took double money, and Benjamin; and rose up, and went down to Egypt, and stood before Joseph. And he asked them of their welfare, and said, "Is your father well, the old man of whom ye spake? Is he yet alive?" And they answered, "Our father is in good health, he is yet alive." And they bowed down their heads, and made obeisance.

And he lifted up his eyes, and saw his brother Benjamin, his mother's son, and said, "Is this your younger brother, of whom ye spake unto me?" And Joseph made haste for his bowels did yearn upon his brother: and he sought where to weep; and he entered into his chamber and wept there.

And he washed his face and went out, and said, "Set on bread." And they set on for him by himself, and for them by themselves, and for the Egyptians, which did eat with him, by themselves.

And he took and sent messes unto them from before him, but Benjamin's mess was five times as much as any of theirs.

And Joseph commanded the steward of his house, saying, "Fill the men's sacks with food, and put every man's money in his sack's mouth, and put my silver cup in the sack of the youngest."

As soon as the morning was light, the men were sent away, they and their asses. Joseph said unto his steward, "Up, follow after them and say, 'Wherefore have ye rewarded evil for good? Wherefore have ye taken the money and my lord's silver cup?' "

And he overtook them, and he spake unto them these same words. And they said unto him, "God forbid that thy servants should do according to this thing! With whomsoever the cup be found, both let him die, and we also will be my lord's bondmen."

Then they speedily took every man his sack to the ground, and the steward searched, and the cup was found in Benjamin's sack.

Then they rent their clothes and returned to the city.

And Judah said unto Joseph, "What shall we say unto our

lord or how shall we clear ourselves? We have a father, an old man, and Benjamin is the child of his old age, a little one; and his brother is dead, and he alone is left of his mother, and his father loveth him. Now, therefore, when I come to thy servant my father, and the lad be not with us, seeing that his life is bound up in the lad's life, it shall come to pass that he will die. Now, therefore, I pray thee, let thy servant abide instead of the lad a bondman to my lord; and let the lad go up with his brethren."

And Joseph could not refrain himself, and he cried, "Cause every man to go out from me." And there stood no man with him, while Joseph came himself down unto his brethren.

And Joseph said unto his brethren, "I am Joseph; come near to me, I pray you." And they came near. And he said, "I am Joseph your brother, whom you sold into Egypt. Now therefore be not grieved, nor angry with yourselves, that ye sold me hither: for God did send me before you to preserve life. So now it was not you that sent me hither, but God: and he hath made me a father to Pharaoh, and lord of all his house. Haste ye, and go up to my father, and say, 'Thus saith thy son Joseph, God hath made me Lord of all Egypt: come down unto me, and thou shalt dwell in the land of Goshen, and thou shalt be near unto me, thou, and thy children, and thy children's children, and thy flocks, and thy herds, and all that thou hast: and there will I nourish thee; for yet there are five years of famine.'" And he fell upon his brother Benjamin's neck. Moreover he kissed all his brethren, and wept upon them.

So his brethren departed: and came unto Jacob, saying, "Joseph is yet alive, and he is governor over all the land of Egypt."

And Israel said, "It is enough: Joseph my son is yet alive: I will go and see him before I die."

And the sons of Israel carried Jacob their father, and their little ones, and their wives, and they took their cattle and their goods, and came into Egypt. And Joseph made ready his chariot, and went up to meet his father, and he fell on his neck, and wept.

Richard Feverel and the Hay-Rick*

GEORGE MEREDITH

OCTOBER shone royally on Richard's fourteenth birthday. The brown beechwoods and golden birches glowed to a brilliant sun. Banks of moveless clouds hung about the horizon, mounded to the west where slept the wind,—promise of a great day for Raynham Abbey to celebrate the birthday of Sir Austin Feverel's son and heir. Already archery booths and cricketing tents were rising on the lower grounds towards the river, whither the lads of Bursley and Lobourne, in boats and in carts, came merrily jogging to match themselves anew. The whole park was beginning to be astir and resound with holiday cries. For Sir Austin could be a popular man when he chose. Half the village of Lobourne was seen trooping through the avenues of the park. Fiddlers and gypsies clamored at the gates for admission. White smocks and gray, surmounted by hats of serious brim, and now and then a scarlet cloak, dotted the grassy sweeps to the levels.

And all the time the hero of these festivities, Richard Feverel himself, was flying farther and farther away from Raynham, losing himself from the sight of men in company with his reluctant friend and obedient serf, Ripton Thompson, who kept asking what they were to do and where they were going, and suggesting that the lads of Lobourne would be calling them to join in the sports, and Sir Austin would be requiring their presence. Richard paid no attention to Ripton's remonstrances. For

*George Meredith (1828-1909) was one of the great novelists in the latter days of Queen Victoria. He followed the famous group which included Dickens, Thackeray, and George Eliot. Arranged from *The Ordeal of Richard Feverel.*

FROM THE TOWER WINDOW

Richard had been requested by his father to submit to medical examination like a boor enlisting for a soldier, and he was in great wrath. He was flying as though he would have flown from the shameful thought of what had been asked of him. The two boys had the dog with them and had borrowed a couple of guns at the bailiff's farm. Off they trotted through the depths of the wood, Ripton following wherever his friend chose to lead. They were beating about for birds, but the birds on the Raynham estate were found singularly cunning, and repeatedly eluded the aim of these prime shots, so they pushed their expedition into the lands of their neighbors, happily oblivious that the law forbids as a criminal trespass, the shooting of game on another's land, unconscious too that they were poaching on the demesne of the notorious Farmer Blaize. Farmer Blaize hated poachers, and especially young chaps poaching who did it mostly from impudence. He heard the audacious shots popping right and left, and going forth to have a glimpse at the intruders, swore he would teach my gentlemen a thing, lords or no lords. Richard had brought down a beautiful cock-pheasant, and was exulting over it, when the farmer's portentous figure burst upon them cracking an avenging horse-whip. His salute was ironical.

"Havin' good sport, gentlemen, are ye? Havin' good sport?"

"Just bagged a splendid bird!" radiant Richard informed him.

"Oh!" Farmer Blaize gave an admonitory flick of the whip. "Tell ye what 'tis!" He changed his banter to business. "That bird's mine! Now you jest hand him over, and sheer off, you damn young scoundrels! I know ye!"

Richard opened his eyes.

"If you wants to be horsewhipped, you'll stay where you are!" continued the farmer.

"Then we'll stay," quoth Richard.

"Good! so be't! If you will have it, have it, my men!" And sweetch went the mighty whip, well swayed. The boys tried to close with him. He kept his distance and lashed without mercy. Black blood was made by Farmer Blaize that day! The boys wriggled in spite of themselves. It was like a relentless serpent coiling and biting and stinging their young veins to madness. Probably they felt the disgrace of the contortions they were made to go through more than the pain, but the pain was fierce, for the farmer laid about from a practiced arm and did not consider that he had done enough till he was well breathed and his ruddy jowl inflamed. He paused to receive the cock-pheasant full in his face. "Take your beastly bird," cried Richard.

Shameful as it was to retreat, there was but that course open to the boys. They decided to surrender the field.

"Look! you big brute," Richard shook his gun, hoarse with passion, "I'd have shot you if I'd been loaded."

This threat exasperated Farmer Blaize and he pressed the pursuit in time to bestow a few farewell stripes. At the hedge they parleyed a minute, the farmer to inquire if they had had a mortal good tanning and were satisfied, for when they wanted a further instalment of the same they were to come for it to Belthorpe Farm, and there it was kept in pickle! The boys meantime exploded in menaces and threats of vengeance, on which the farmer contemptuously turned his back. Ripton had already stocked an armful of stones for the enjoyment of a little skirmishing. Richard however knocked them all out, saying, "No! Gentlemen don't fling stones. Leave that to the blackguards!"

"Just one shy at him," pleaded Ripton.

"No," said Richard imperatively, "no stones," and marched briskly away. Ripton followed with a sigh. But Richard's blood was poisoned. A sweeping and consummate vengeance for the indignity alone should satisfy him. Something tremendous must be done and done without delay. At one moment he thought of killing all the farmer's cattle; next of killing him; challenging him to single combat with the arms, and according to the fashion of gentlemen. But the farmer was a coward; he would refuse. Then he, Richard Feverel, would stand by the farmer's bedside, and rouse him, rouse him to fight with powder and ball in his own chamber, in the cowardly midnight, where he might tremble, but dare not refuse.

"Lord!" cried simple Ripton, while these hopeful plots were raging in his comrade's brain. "How I wish you'd have let me shy one at him, Ricky! I'd feel quite jolly if I'd spanked him once."

To these exclamations Richard was deaf, and he trudged steadily forward facing but one object. After tearing through innumerable hedges, leaping fences, jumping dykes, penetrating brambly copses, and getting dirty, ragged and tired, Ripton awoke from his dream of Farmer Blaize to the vivid consciousness of hunger; and this grew with the rapidity of light upon him, till in the course of another minute he was enduring the extremes of famine, and ventured to question his leader whither he was being conducted. Raynham was now out of sight. They were a long way down the valley, miles from Lobourne, in a country of sour pools, yellow brooks, rank pasturage, desolate heath. Solitary cows were seen; the smoke of a mud cottage; a cart piled with peat; a donkey grazing at leisure; geese gabbling by a horse-pond; uncooked things that a famishing boy cannot possibly care for. Ripton was in despair—

"Where are you going to?" he inquired and halted resolutely.

Richard now broke his silence to reply, "Anywhere."

"Anywhere!" Ripton repeated, "but aren't you awful hungry?"

"No," was Richard's brief response.

"Not hungry!" Ripton's amazement lent him increased

vehemence. "Why you haven't had anything to eat since breakfast! I declare I'm starving. Come, tell us where you're going."

Richard lifted his head, surveyed the position, and exclaim-
ing "Here!" dropped down on a withered bank, leaving Ripton
to contemplate him as a puzzle whose every new move was a
worse perplexity. But Master Ripton Thompson was naturally
loyal. The idea of turning off and forsaking his friend never
once crossed his mind, though his condition was desperate, and
his friend's behavior that of a Bedlamite. He announced several
times impatiently that they would be too late for dinner. His
friend did not budge. Dinner seemed nothing to him. There
he sat plucking grass and patting the old dog's nose as if incapable
of conceiving what a thing hunger was. Ripton at last flung
himself down beside the silent boy, accepting his fate.

Now it chanced just then that a smart shower fell with the
sinking sun, and the wet sent two strangers for shelter into the
lane behind the hedge where the boys reclined. One was a travel-
ling tinker, who lit a pipe and spread a tawny umbrella. The
other was a burly young countryman, pipeless and tentless.
They saluted with a nod, and began recounting for each other's
benefit the day-long doings of the weather.

Ripton solaced his wretchedness by watching them through
the briar hedge. He saw the tinker stroking a white cat, and
appealing to her every now and then, as his missus, and he thought
that a curious sight. Speed-the-Plough was stretched at full
length with his boots in the rain and his head amidst the tinker's
pots, smoking, profoundly thinking.

Said the tinker, "Times is bad!"

His companion assented, "Sure-ly!"

"But everything somehow comes round right," resumed the
tinker. "Where's the good o' moping? I sees it all come right
and tight. T'other day I was as nigh ship-wrecked as the prophet
Paul. We pitched and tossed. I thinks, down we're a-going.

FROM THE TOWER WINDOW

But God's above the devil, and here I am, ye see."

Speed-the-Plough lurched round on his elbow and regarded him indifferently. "God ben't al'ays above the devil, or I shoo'n't be scrapin' my heels wi' nothin' to do, and, what's warse, nothin' to eat. Why, look heer. Heer's a darned bad case. I threshed for Varmer Blaize—Blaize o' Belthorpe. Varmer Blaize misses pilkins. He swears our chaps steal pilkins. 'Twarn't me steals 'em. What do he take and go and do? He takes and turns us off, me and another, neck and crop, to scuffle about and starve, for all he keers. God warn't above the devil then, I thinks. Not nohow as I can see!"

The tinker shook his head and said that was a bad case.

"And you can't mend it," added Speed-the-Plough. "It's bad, and there it be. But I'll tell ye what, master. Bad wants payin' for." He nodded and winked mysteriously. "Bad has its wages as well as honest work, I'm thinkin'. Varmer Blaize I owes a grudge to. And I shud like to stick a match in his hay-rick some dry, windy night." Speed-the-Plough screwed up an eye villainously. "He wants hittin' jest where the pocket is, do Varmer Blaize, and he'll cry out, 'O Lor,' Varmer Blaize will, if ye hit him jest there."

The tinker sent a rapid succession of white clouds from his mouth and said that firing Farmer Blaize's rick would be taking the devil's side of a bad case. Speed-the-Plough observed ener-

59

getically that if Farmer Blaize was on the other side, he preferred to be on the devil's side.

There was a young gentleman close by who thought with him. The hope of Raynham had lent a careless, half-compelled attention to the foregoing conversation. He now started to his feet and came tearing through the briar hedge, calling out for the men to direct him the nearest road to Bursley. The tinker was kindling preparations for his tea under the tawny umbrella. A loaf was set forth, on which Ripton's eyes fastened ravenously. Speed-the-Plough volunteered the information that Bursley was a good three miles from where they stood.

"I'll give you a half-crown for that loaf, my good fellow," said Richard to the tinker.

"It's a bargain," quoth the tinker, "eh, missus?"

His cat replied by humping her back at the dog.

The half-crown was tossed down, and Ripton collared the loaf.

In a short time Speed-the-Plough and the tinker were following the two lads on the road to Bursley, while a horizontal blaze shot across the autumn land from the western edge of the rain-cloud. And more there was that passed between the boys and Speed-the-Plough on the road of a nature extremely interesting.

Search for the missing boys had been made everywhere over Raynham, and Sir Austin was in grievous discontent. No one had seen them. All the sports of the day,—cricket, bowling, archery contests on the green, all without him whom the festival had been designed to honor. At dinner in the evening, the company of honored friends, aunts, uncles, cousins, sat all about the great table and naught there was but a vacant chair and napkin in place of Richard. By ten at night the poor show ended, the rooms were dark and the guests departed.

It was late when old Benson the butler tolled out intelligence to Sir Austin, "Master Richard has returned."

"Well?" said the baronet.

FROM THE TOWER WINDOW

"He complains of being hungry," the butler hesitated with a look of solemn disgust.

"Let him eat."

The boys were in the vortex of a partridge pie when Adrian Harley strolled in upon them. Adrian was Richard's cousin, a youth wise in the ways of the world, though perhaps not too scrupulous in his moral tone. He had been chosen by Sir Austin to superintend the education of his motherless son. Adrian found Richard uproarious, his cheeks flushed and his eyes brilliant, while Ripton looked very much like a rogue on the tremble lest he be detected in some crime.

"Good sport, gentlemen, I trust to hear?" began Adrian in his quiet banter.

"Ha, ha! I say, Rip: 'Havin' good sport, gentlemen, are ye?' You remember the farmer! We're going to have some first rate sport. Oh well! we haven't much show of birds. We shot for pleasure and returned them to the proprietors. But Rip and I have had a beautiful day. We've made new acquaintances. We've seen the world. First there's a farmer who warns everybody, gentleman and beggar, off his premises. Next there's a tinker and a ploughman who think that God is always fighting with the devil which shall command the kingdoms of the earth—"

Here a hideous and silencing frown from Ripton interrupted Richard's words. Adrian watched the innocent youths and knew that there was talking under the table. Soon Uncle Algernon, the one-legged veteran, shambled in to see his nephew, and his genial presence brought out a little more of the plot.

"Look here, uncle," said Richard. "Would you let a churlish old brute of a farmer strike you without making him suffer for it?"

"I fancy I should return the compliment," replied his uncle.

"Of course you would. So would I. And he shall suffer for it!"

But in the midst of all this riot there was one subject at Richard's heart about which he was reserved. Too proud to inquire how his father had taken his absence, he burned to hear whether he was in disgrace. At last when the boy declared a desire to wish his father good-night, Adrian had to tell him that he was to go straight to bed from the supper table. Young Richard's face fell at that and his gaiety forsook him, for he had a deep and reverent affection for his father. He marched to his room without another word.

At midnight the house breathed sleep. Sir Austin put on his cloak and cap and took the lamp as he always did to make his rounds of the place. He ascended the stairs and bent his steps leisurely toward the chamber where his son was lying in the left wing of the Abbey. At the end of the gallery which led to it, he discovered a dim light. Doubting it an illusion, Sir Austin accelerated his pace. A slight descent brought the baronet into the passage and he beheld a candle standing outside his son's chamber. At the same moment a door closed hastily. He entered Richard's room. The boy was absent. The bed was unpressed, nothing to show that he had been there that night. Sir Austin felt vaguely apprehensive. He determined to go and ask the boy Thompson, as he called Ripton, what was known to him.

The chamber assigned to Master Ripton overlooked the valley toward Belthorpe farm. Sir Austin found the door ajar and the interior dark. To his surprise Ripton's couch as revealed by the rays of his lamp was likewise vacant. He was turning back when he fancied he heard whispering in the room. Sir Austin cloaked the lamp and trod silently toward the window. The heads of his son Richard and the boy Thompson were seen crouched against the glass holding excited converse together. Sir Austin listened, but he listened to a language of which he possessed not the key. Their talk was of fire and of delay, of a farmer's huge wrath, of violence exercised upon gentlemen, and of vengeance. Over Lobourne and the valley lay black night and innumerable stars.

"How jolly I feel!" exclaimed Ripton. "But I think that

fellow has pocketed his guinea and jumped his job."

"If he has," said Richard slowly, "I'll go and I'll do it myself."

"You would?" returned Master Ripton. "Well I'm hanged! But I say, do you think we shall ever be found out?"

"I don't think about it," said Richard, all his faculties bent on signs from Lobourne.

"Well but," Ripton persisted, "suppose we are found out?"

"If we are, I must pay for it."

Sir Austin breathed the better for this reply. He was beginning to gather a clue to the dialogue. His son was engaged in a plot, and was, moreover, the leader in the plot.

"What was the fellow's name?" inquired Ripton.

His companion answered, "Tom Bakewell."

"I tell you what," continued Ripton, "you let it all out to your cousin and uncle at supper. Didn't you see me frown?"

"Yes, and felt your kick under the table. But it doesn't matter. Rady's safe and Uncle never blabs. Besides, you've got nothing to do with it if we are found out."

"Haven't I though? I didn't stick in the box of matches, but I'm an accomplice, that's clear. Besides, do you think I should leave you to bear it all on your own shoulders? I'm not that sort of a chap, Ricky."

A sensation of infinite melancholy overcame the poor father. This motherless child, for whom he had prayed nightly in such a fervor and humbleness to God, the dangers were about him, the temptations thick upon him. He was half disposed to arrest the two conspirators on the spot, and make them confess and absolve themselves, but it seemed to him better to leave his son to work out the matter himself, as was his custom, trusting all to the victory of the good he had been so earnestly implanting in the boy from his infancy.

The valley still lay black beneath the large autumnal stars and the exclamations of the boys were becoming fevered and impatient. By and by one insisted that he had seen a twinkle in the right direction. Both boys started to their feet.

"He's done it!" cried Richard in great heat. "Now you may say old Blaize'll soon be old Blazes, Rip. I hope he's asleep."

"I'm sure he's snoring! Look there! He's alight fast enough. He's dry! He'll burn! Lord! Isn't it just beginning to flare up?"

The farmer's grounds were indeed gradually standing out in sombre shadows.

"I'll fetch my telescope," said Richard. Ripton, somehow not liking to be left alone, caught hold of him.

"No! Don't go and lose the best of it. Here, I'll throw open the window and we can see."

The window was flung open and the boys stretched half their bodies out of it, Ripton appearing to devour the rising flames with his mouth, Richard with his eyes.

Opaque and statuesque stood the figure of the baronet behind them. The wind was low. Dense masses of smoke hung amid the darting snakes of fire, and a red, malign, light was on the neighboring leafage. No figures could be seen. Apparently the flames had nothing to contend against, for they were making terrible strides into the darkness.

"Oh!" shouted Richard, overcome by excitement. "If I had my telescope! We must have it! Let me go and fetch it! I will!"

The boys struggled together, and Sir Austin left them.

In the morning that followed this night great gossip was interchanged between Raynham and Lobourne. The village told how Farmer Blaize of Belthorpe Farm had his rick villainously set fire to; his stables had caught fire, himself had been all but roasted alive in the attempt to rescue his cattle, of which numbers had perished in the flames. A formal report of the catastrophe went on to tell of certain ludicrous damage done to the farmer's breeches and the necessity for applying certain cooling applications to a part of the farmer's person. Sir Austin read the report without a smile. The two boys listened very demurely as to an ordinary newspaper incident; only when the report particularized just what garments were damaged, and the unwonted distressing position Farmer Blaize was reduced to in bed, a fit of sneezing laid hold of Master Ripton, and Richard bit his lip and burst into loud laughter, Ripton joining him lost to consequences.

"I trust you feel for this poor man," said Sir Austin to his son somewhat sternly. He saw no sign of feeling.

At every minute of the day Ripton was thrown into sweats of suspicion that discovery was imminent by some stray remark of Adrian's. Adrian played with the boys as though they had been fish caught on his hook.

"By the way, my friends," he observed once, "you met two gentlemen of the road in your explorations yesterday, didn't you? A tinker and a ploughman, I think you said. Now if I were a magistrate of the county, like Sir Miles Papworth, my suspicions would light upon those gentlemen."

The boys tried to evade discussion but the hook was in their gills, and Adrian always drew them skilfully back to the subject.

"Transportation is the punishment for rick-burning," he said solemnly. "They shave your head. You are manacled. Your diet is sour bread and cheese-parings. You work in strings of twenties and thirties. Arson is branded on your back in an enormous A."

The boys, after deep consultation agreed upon a course of conduct which was loudly to express their sympathy for Farmer Blaize. Adrian relished their novel tactics sharply and led them to lengths of lamentation for the farmer. Ripton was fast becoming a coward and Richard a liar when next morning there came to Raynham Abbey, Austin Wentworth, another cousin, a young man who was greatly loved and respected there, but of straightforward, honest disposition, quite different from Adrian's. He brought news that one, Mr. Thomas Bakewell, had been arrested on suspicion of the crime of arson and lodged in jail awaiting the magisterial pleasure of Sir Miles Papworth. Austin's eye rested on Richard as he spoke these terrible tidings.

As soon as they could escape the boys got away together to an obscure corner of the park and there took counsel.

"Whatever shall we do now?" asked Ripton of his leader.

Scorpion girt with fire was never in a more terrible prison than poor Ripton, around whom the raging element he had assisted to create seemed to be drawing momentarily narrower circles.

"There's only one chance," said Richard folding his arms resolutely. "We must rescue that fellow from jail. We must manage to get a file in to him and a rope."

Austin Wentworth had the reputation of being the poor man's friend. He went straight to Tom Bakewell in jail and engaged in man-to-man conversation with him like a gentleman and a Christian. When he rose to go, Tom begged permission to shake his hand and said, "Take and tell young master up at the abbey that I ain't the chap to peach. He'll understand. He's a young gentleman as 'll make any man do as he wants 'em. But I ain't a blackguard. Tell him that, sir."

Austin was not clever like Adrian; he always went the direct road to his object, so instead of beating about the bush with the boys and setting them on the alert, crammed to the muzzle with lies, he came straight out and said, "Tom Bakewell told me to let you know he does not intend to peach on you," and left them.

Richard repeated the intelligence to Ripton, who cried aloud that Tom was a brick.

"He sha'n't suffer for it," said Richard.

The boys had examined the outer walls of the jail and arrived at the conclusion that Tom's escape might be managed if Tom had spirit and the rope and file could by any means be got to him. But to do this somebody must gain admittance to his cell. The boys decided to ask Austin Wentworth to do this. Ripton procured the file at one shop in Bursley and Richard the rope at another, with such masterly cunning did they lay their measures for the avoidance of every possible chance of detection. And better to assure this, in a wood outside Bursley, Richard stripped to his shirt and wound the rope round his body. It was a severe stroke when after all their stratagem and trouble, Austin Wentworth refused the office the boys had designed for him. Time pressed. In a few days poor Tom would have to face the redoubtable Sir Miles, and get committed, for there were rumors of overwhelming evidence to convict him, and Farmer Blaize's wrath was unappeasable. Again and again Richard begged his cousin to help him in this extremity. Austin smiled on him.

"My dear Ricky," said he, "there are two ways of getting out of a scrape,—a long way and a short way. When you've tried the roundabout method and failed come to me and I'll show you the straight route."

Richard was too entirely bent upon the roundabout method to consider the advice more than empty words, and only ground his teeth at Austin's refusal. He told Ripton that they must do it themselves to which Ripton heavily assented.

On the day preceding poor Tom's doomed appearance before the magistrate, the two boys entered the small shop of Dame Bakewell, Tom's mother. There they desperately purchased tea, sugar, candles and comfits of every description, as an excuse for their presence until the shop was empty of customers. They then hurried Dame Bakewell into her little back parlor, where Richard tore open his shirt and revealed the coils of rope and Ripton displayed the file. They told the astonished woman that the rope and the file were instruments to free her son and that there existed no other means on earth to save him. Richard with the utmost earnestness tried to persuade Dame Bakewell to disrobe and wind the rope around her own person, and Ripton sought eloquently to induce her to secrete the file. Dame Bakewell resolutely objected to the rope, but she was at length persuaded, though much against her will, to accept the file. This she carried secretly to her son. Tom however turned up his nose at the file and refused to try to make an escape. At this news, Richard was in despair. Moreover, just now Ripton was sent for to go home to London and Richard was left to face the whole matter alone.

When affairs were at this pass, Austin Wentworth went to consult with Adrian. But Adrian was little concerned about how the course Richard was pursuing would work out for good or evil in the boy's own mind and heart. He was anxious only to keep them all free from the action of the law. And he threw out the hint to Austin that he had already fixed matters up by means of a little secret dealing with the farmer's chief witness, so that there was no danger of anyone's being punished for the crime. This by no means satisfied Austin. His concern was less that Richard should escape punishment, than that he should act like a man.

A little laurel-shaded temple of white marble looked out on the river from a knoll bordering the Raynham beechwoods and was dubbed by Adrian, Daphne's Bower. To this spot Richard had retired and there Austin found him with his head buried in his hands, a picture of desperation whose last shift has been defeated.

"Well, Ricky, have you tried your own way of rectifying this business?" asked Austin.

"I have done everything."

"And failed!"

There was a pause, then Richard tried to evade the responsibility.

"Failed because Tom Bakewell's a coward!"

"I suppose, poor fellow," said Austin in his kind way, "he doesn't want to get into a deeper mess. I don't think he's a coward."

"He is a coward," cried Richard. "Do you think if I had a file, I would stay in prison? I'd be out the first night. He's a coward and deserves his fate. I've no compassion for a coward."

"Nor I much," said Austin. "I never

met a coward myself. But I've heard of one or two. One let an innocent man die for a crime he himself had committed."

"How base!" exclaimed the boy.

"Yes, it was bad." Austin agreed. "I have read also in the confessions of a celebrated philosopher that in his youth he committed some petty theft and then accused a young servant-girl of his own crime, permitting her to be condemned and dismissed."

"What a coward!" shouted Richard. "And he confessed it?"

"You may read it yourself. Would you have done so much?"

Richard faltered. No! He admitted that he could never have told people.

"Then who is to call that man a coward?" said Austin. "He paid the penalty for the wrong he had done as all who give way in moments of weakness and are not cowards must do. The coward chooses to think 'God does not see. I shall escape.' He who is not a coward, but has done wrong, knows that God has seen all, and it is not so hard a task for him to make his heart bare to the world. Worse, I should fancy it, to know myself an impostor when men praised me."

Richard suddenly hung his head.

"So I think you're wrong, Ricky, in calling this poor fellow Tom a coward because he refuses to try your means of escape. He has not acted like a coward in refusing to tell on you."

Richard was dumb. If he avowed Tom's manly behavior, then he would have to see Richard Feverel in a new light. Whereas, by insisting that Tom was a coward Richard Feverel was the injured one and in no way to blame. Austin had but a blind notion of the fierceness with which the conflict raged in young Richard. But happily Richard's nature wanted little more than an indication of the proper track and then he said in a subdued voice, "Tell me what I can do, Austin."

Austin put his hand on the boy's shoulder.

"You must go down to Farmer Blaize. You will know

what to say to him when you're standing there before him."

The boy bit his lip and frowned. "Ask a favor of that big brute, Austin? I can't!"

"Just tell him the whole truth."

"But, Austin," the boy pleaded, "I shall have to ask a favor of him. I shall have to beg him to help off Tom Bakewell. How can I ask a favor of a brute I hate? I shall hardly be able to keep my hands off him."

"Surely you've punished him enough, boy," said Austin.

"He struck me!" Richard's lip quivered.

"But you poached on his grounds."

"I'll pay him for his loss, but I won't ask a favor of him."

Austin looked at the boy steadily. "You prefer to receive a favor from poor Tom Bakewell? To save yourself an unpleasantness you permit a country lad to sacrifice himself for you. I confess I should not have so much pride."

"Pride!" shouted Richard stung by the taunt, and set his sight hard at the blue ridges of the hills.

Not knowing for the moment what else to do, Austin drew a picture of Tom in prison. Visions of a grinning lout, unkempt, coarse, rose before Richard and afflicted him with the strangest sensations of disgust and comicality, mixed up with pity and remorse,—a sort of twisted pathos. There lay Tom, hobnail Tom! a bacon-munching, reckless, beer-swilling animal and yet a man, capable of devotion and unselfishness. The boy's better spirit was touched, and it kindled his imagination to realize the abject figure of poor clodpole Tom, and surround it with a halo of mournful light. His soul was alive. Feelings he had never known streamed in upon him, an unwonted tenderness, an embracing humor, a consciousness of some ineffable glory. Toward clodpole Tom he felt just then a loving kindness beyond what he felt for any living creature. He laughed at him and wept over him. He prized him while he shrank from him. It was a genial strife of the angel in him with constituents less divine. But the angel was uppermost and won the day.

Austin sat by the boy unaware of the tumult he had stirred. Little of it was perceptible in Richard's countenance. Finally he jumped up, saying: "I'll go at once to old Blaize and tell him."

Austin grasped his hand and together they issued out of Daphne's Bower.

Farmer Blaize was not so astonished at the visit of Richard Feverel as that young gentleman had expected him to be. The farmer seated in his easy chair in the little low-roofed parlor of an old-fashioned farm-house, with a long clay pipe on the table at his elbow and a veteran pointer at his feet, had already given audience to Sir Austin Feverel himself who came to him secretly and frankly confessed the whole matter. Thereupon Farmer Blaize had decided that he would only give up the prosecution in exchange for three hundred pounds compensation to his pocket, a spoken apology from the prime offender, Master Richard, and a solemn promise that no one should try to bribe his witnesses to change their testimony. Sir Austin had readily promised him full indemnity in money for his loss, a satisfactory apology from his son and the assurance that no one would tamper with his witnesses.

Richard was received by a pretty little girl with the roses of thirteen springs in her cheeks and abundant beautiful bright tresses. She tripped before the boy and led him to the parlor, loitering shyly by the farmer's arm chair to steal a look at the handsome new-comer. She was introduced to Richard as the farmer's niece, Lucy Desborough, and Farmer Blaize said much in her praise laughing and chuckling, perhaps intending thus to give his visitor time to recover his composure. His diversion only irritated and confused our shame-eaten youth. Richard's intention had been to come to the farmer's threshold, to summon the farmer thither and in a loud and haughty tone, then and there to take upon himself the whole burden of the charge against

Tom Bakewell. Farmer Blaize was quite at his ease, nowise in a hurry. He spoke of the weather and the harvest. Richard blinked hard. In a moment of silence he cried.

"Mr. Blaize, I have come to tell you that I am the person who set fire to your rick the other night."

An odd contraction formed about the farmer's mouth. He changed his posture and said, "Aye, that's what ye're come to tell me, sir! Then, my lad, ye've come to tell me a lie!"

"You dare to call me a liar!" cried Richard starting up with clenched fist. "You have twice insulted me. I would have apologized to have got off that fellow in prison. I would have degraded myself that another man should not suffer for my deed, and you take this opportunity of insulting me afresh. You're a coward, sir. Nobody but a coward would have insulted me in his own house."

"Sit ye down! Sit ye down, young master," said the farmer. "Don't ye be hasty. If ye hadn't been hasty t' other day we should a been friends. I should be sorry to reckon you out a liar. What I say is that as you say an't the truth."

Richard angrily reseated himself. The farmer spoke sense, and the boy after his late interview with Austin had become capable of perceiving vaguely that a towering passion hardly justifies one in pursuing a wrong course of conduct.

"Come," continued the farmer not unkindly, "what else have you to say?"

The boy blinked. This was a bitter cup for him to drink.

"I came to say that I regretted the revenge I had taken on you for you striking me. You shall be repaid for your loss, and I should be very much obliged, very much obliged," he stammered, "if you would be so kind (fancy a Feverel asking this big brute to be so kind), so kind as to do me the favor,—to exert yourself—to endeavor to—hem! (there's no saying it!) What I want to ask is whether you would have the kindness,—Well then I want you, Mr. Blaize, if you don't mind, will you help me to get this man Bakewell off his punishment?"

To do Farmer Blaize justice, he waited very patiently for the boy.

"Hum," said he. "But if you did it you know, and Tom's innocent, we sha'n't make him out guilty. Do you still hold to it, you set fire to the rick?"

"The blame is mine," quoth Richard with the loftiness of a patriot of old Rome.

"Na, na!" the straightforward farmer put him aside. "Ye did do it or ye didn't do it,—yes or no."

Thrust into a corner, Richard said, "I did it."

Farmer Blaize reached his hand to the bell. It was answered in an instant by little Lucy, who received orders to fetch in a dependent at Belthorpe going by the name of the Bantam.

"Now," said the farmer, "these be my principles. I'm a plain man, Mr. Feverel. Be above board with me and you'll find me handsome. Be underhanded and I'm a ugly customer. I'll show you I've no animosity. Your father pays, you apologize. That's enough for me. But the Bantam saw what happened t'other night. It's no use your denyin' that evidence."

Just then Miss Lucy ushered in the Bantam. In build of body, gait and stature, Giles Jinkson, the Bantam, was a tolerably

fair representative of the elephant. He had been the first to give
the clue at Belthorpe on the night of the conflagration and he
may, therefore, have seen poor Tom retreating stealthily from the
scene as he said he did. Leastwise, he was the farmer's principal
witness. There he stood and tugged his forelocks to the company.

"Now," said the farmer, with the utmost confidence. "Tell
this young gentleman what ye saw on the night of the fire, Bantam."

The Bantam jerked a bit of a bow to his patron, and then
swung around, fully shutting off all view of the farmer from
Richard. Richard fixed his eyes on the floor while the Bantam
told his story. But when the recital reached the point where
the Bantam affirmed he had seen Tom Bakewell with his own
eyes, Richard was amazed to find himself being mutely addressed
by a series of intensely significant grimaces, signs and winks.

"What do you mean? Why are you making those faces at
me?" cried the boy indignantly.

"Bain't makin' no faces at nobody," growled the sulky elephant.

"You never saw Tom Bakewell set fire to that rick! How
could you see who it was on a pitch-dark night?"

The suborned elephant was staggered. He had meant to
telegraph to the young gentleman that he was loyal and true
to certain gold pieces that had been given him and that in the
right place and at the right time he should prove so.

"A thowt I seen 'un then," muttered the Bantam.

"Thought!" the farmer bellowed. "Thought! Devil take ye.
Ye took yer oath on it! Say what ye saw and none o' your
thoughts! Thinkin' an't evidence! Ye saw Tom Bakewell fire
that there rick. You're a witness. Damn your thoughts!"

Thus adjured, the Bantam hitched his breeches. What on
earth the young gentleman meant by making public his private
signals he was at a loss to speculate. He determined at length
after much ploughing and harrowing through obstinate shocks of
hair, to be not altogether positive as to the person he had seen.

FROM THE TOWER WINDOW

It is possible that he became thereby more truthful than he had previously been, for the night had been so dark that you could not see your hand before your face. The party he had taken for Tom Bakewell, he said, might have been the young gentleman present. He could not swear which it was.

"But you swore to't, 'twas Tom Bakewell!" the farmer roared.

"No," said the Bantam, with a twitch of the shoulder and an angular jerk of the elbow. "Not upon oath!" A cunning distinction, that between swearing and not swearing upon oath! No sooner had the Bantam ceased than Farmer Blaize jumped up from his chair and made a fine effort to lift him out of the room from the point of his toe. Richard would have preferred not to laugh but his dignity gave way and he let fly a shout.

"They're liars, every one!" cried the farmer. "Now look ye here, Mr. Feverel! You've been a-tampering with my witness! It's no use denyin'! I say ye have, sir! The Bantam's been bribed!" and he shivered his pipe with an energetic thump on the table. "He's been corrupted, my principal witness. Oh it's damn cunning but it won't do the trick. I'll transport Tom Bakewell now sure as a gun. Sorry you haven't seen how to treat me square and honest! I'd ha' 'scused you, sir. You're a boy and 'll learn better. But you've bribed my witness. Now you must stand yer luck, all o' ye. I will have the truth!"

Richard stood up and replied, "Very well, Mr. Blaize."

"I believe yer father," went on the farmer.

"What!" cried Richard, with astonishment. "You have seen my father! My father knows of this?"

Farmer Blaize pulled the bell. " 'Comp'ny the young gentleman out, Lucy," he waved to the little damsel in the doorway. "And, Mr. Richard, ye might have made a friend o' me, sir, and it's not too late so to do. I'm not cruel, but I hate lies. Now if ye'll come down to me and speak truth before the trial—if it's only five minutes before, or if Sir Austin, who's a gentleman, 'll

75

say there's been no bribin' my witnesses, if he'll give his word for it,—well and good, I'll do my best to help off Tom Bakewell. If not I'll see the fellow transported. Good afternoon, sir."

Richard marched hastily out of the room and through the garden, never so much as deigning a glance at his wistful little guide, who hung at the garden gate to watch him up the lane, wondering a world of fancies about the handsome, proud boy.

To have determined upon an act something akin to heroism, and to have fulfilled it by lying heartily, seems a sad downfall. But good seed is long ripening, a good boy is not made in a minute. Enough that the seed was in him.

Richard chafed on his road to Raynham at the scene he had just endured, and the figure of Belthorpe's fat tenant burnt like hot copper on the tablet of his brain, insufferably condescending and what was worse, in the right.

After dinner that evening Richard and his father were alone for the first time. It was a strange meeting. They seemed to have been separated so long. The father took his son's hand; they sat without a word passing between them. Silence said most. That pressure of his father's hand was eloquent to the boy of how warmly he was beloved. He tried once or twice to steal his hand away, conscious it was melting him. The spirit of his pride and old rebellion whispered him to be hard, unbending, resolute. Hard he had entered his father's study, hard he had met his father's eyes. He could not meet them now.

By degrees an emotion awoke in the boy's bosom. Love is that blessed wand which wins the waters from the hardness of the heart. Richard fought against it for the dignity of old rebellion. The tears would come, hot and struggling over the dams of pride. Shamefully fast they began to fall. He could no longer conceal them or check the sobs. Sir Austin drew him nearer and nearer till the beloved head was on his breast.

An hour afterwards, Adrian Harley, Austin Wentworth and

FROM THE TOWER WINDOW

Algernon Feverel were summoned to the baronet's study. Young Richard's red eyes and the baronet's ruffled demeanor told them that an explanation had taken place and a reconciliation. That was well. A general council was held. Slowly there was drawn from Richard the tale of his recent visit to the farmer and the ridiculous collapse of the Bantam's testimony, which part of the story caused Adrian to choke with laughter. But Richard also told of the farmer's belief that the Bantam had been bribed and the sudden return of his vindictive determination to have Tom transported. Adrian made a very persuasive plea that the Feverel family should now drop the whole matter. Tom Bakewell would not peach on Richard and it was most unlikely that the boy would be drawn into the affair. He argued well, but the basis of his plea being to do the expedient thing, the thing that was easiest regardless of what was right, Sir Austin answered him:

"Expediency is man's wisdom, Adrian. Doing right is God's."

And he rose and left the room saying that he would pay a second visit to Belthorpe, and attempt to straighten out the matter.

Richard saw his father go forth. Then he said slowly:

"Blaize told me that if my father would give his word there had been no tampering with his witnesses, he would believe him and drop the whole matter. My father will give his word."

Adrian was ill at ease. "Then you had better stop him from going," he said.

A moment Richard lingered. In his heart he knew that Adrian had bribed the Bantam to change his testimony. He knew his father never even dreamed of such a thing. If he let him go, his father who was honor's self, would all-unknowingly swear to a lie. It would be easy, so easy. His father would simply give his word, and then Farmer Blaize would drop the whole matter. He, Richard, would never have to swallow his pride again and tell the whole truth. But—his father would swear to a lie!

Sir Austin was in the lane leading to the farm when he heard steps of some one running behind him. It was dark and he shook off the hand that laid hold of his coat, not recognizing his son.

"It's I, sir," said Richard panting. "You mustn't go in there."

"Why not?" said the baronet putting his arm about him.

"Not now," continued the boy. "I will tell you all tonight. I must see the farmer myself. It was my fault, sir; I—lied to him—the liar must eat his lie. Oh, forgive me for disgracing you, sir. I did it—I hope I did it to save Tom Bakewell. Let me go in alone and speak the truth."

"Go, and I will wait for you here," said his father.

The wind that bowed the old elms and shivered the dead leaves in the air, had a voice and a meaning for the baronet during that half hour's lonely pacing up and down under the darkness awaiting his boy's return. The solemn gladness of his heart gave nature a tongue. Through the desolation flying over head, his heart was newly confirmed in its belief in the ultimate victory of good within us.

And so after all his twistings and turnings, Richard took the one straight course and told the truth. The upshot of the whole matter was that Tom was not convicted. He was set free and Sir Austin took him into his own employ where Richard had plenty of opportunity to urge him on to better things than burning ricks. As to Richard himself he felt that he had had a sorry enough experience of what comes from giving way to passion. He wrote his thoughts on that matter to his old friend and accomplice, Rip, who had been paying the penalty for his share of the crime by suffering the gravest mental terrors, living in constant fear lest he should be found out and have to flee to America as the only means of starting life afresh as an innocent gentleman.

And it was necessary for Richard to order Adrian not to call him by his old nickname Ricky any more, for that redoubtable tease took to stopping short at the word Rick which, needless to say, was not a word with which Richard chose to be associated.

FROM THE TOWER WINDOW

EVENING AT THE FARM*
John Townsend Trowbridge

Into the yard the farmer goes,
With grateful heart, at the close of day;
Harness and chain are hung away;
In the wagon-shed stand yoke and plough,
The straw's in the stack, the hay in the mow,
    The cooling dews are falling;—
The friendly sheep their welcome bleat,
The pigs come grunting to his feet,
And the whinnying mare her master knows,
When into the yard the farmer goes,
    His cattle calling,—
    "Co', boss! co', boss! co'! co'! co'!"
While still the cow-boy, far away,
Goes seeking those that have gone astray,—
    "Co', boss! co', boss! co'! co'!"

To supper at last the farmer goes.
The apples are pared, the paper read,
The stories are told, then all to bed.
Without, the crickets' ceaseless song
Makes shrill the silence all night long;
    The heavy dews are falling.
The household sinks to deep repose,
But still in sleep the farm-boy goes
    Singing, calling,—
    "Co', boss! co', boss! co'! co'! co'!"
And oft the milkmaid, in her dreams,
Drums in the pail with the flashing streams,
    Murmuring "So, boss! so!"

*Used by permission of, and special arrangement with, Houghton Mifflin Company, the publishers.

79

How Beowulf Delivered Heorot

Retold from the Old English Epic, Beowulf

Lo! We have heard tell of the might in days of old of the Danish folk-kings, how deeds of daring were done by their athelings. To Hrothgar, beloved folk-king of the Scyldings, was given such glory of war that gladly his kinsfolk obeyed him and great grew his gathering of warriors. Then blithely it burned in his spirit to bid men build him a dwelling, greater than children of men had ever heard tell of, and there within it, to share with young and with old, the good things God gave him. To all the King's kinsmen, far and wide through the mid-earth, was given the task of making fair the folk-hall. Speedily it befell that it was in every wise ready, the greatest of hall-houses, and Hrothgar hailed it by name He'o-rot, the Stag. High on a hill rose the hall, broad-gabled and builded of timber. Gold-bright and glittering its roof, carven and painted its pillars, with antlers of stags bedecked.

FROM THE TOWER WINDOW

Then Hrothgar belied not his pledge. When first there was feasting he gave to his kinsfolk and clansmen collars of gold, with richly wrought rings and treasures at table. Each day did the din of revel resound. High in the hall rang the harps; clear sounded song of the gleemen. So dwelt the warriors in wassail, till that foul fiend and foe to mankind, Grendel, the grim and the greedy, he who went prowling the borders, a roamer, lonely and terrible, heard their rejoicings with envy. This dark demon, huger than human bulk, who yet in the shape of a man trod the track of exile, haunted the misty moorlands, the fastnesses and fens. At night-fall, Grendel fared forth to find that haughty hall-house, and heed how the Ring-Danes had left it. There found he thirty athelings, asleep and fearless of sorrow. Unhallowed wight, grim and greedy, he slew betimes, fierce and pitiless, all those thirty thanes. Then home, exulting in evil, laden with slaughter, he stalked.

The great epic of the Anglo-Saxons was composed in Northern Europe before the Anglo-Saxons came to England, but it shows just how they lived after they settled in England. A *Lament for Beowulf* was written as a choral work by the American composer, Howard Hanson.

At day-break, came Hrothgar's henchmen Heorot to cleanse.
There lo, the mead-hall stood empty of athelings, bench-boards
o'erturned, and signs of a struggle. Sorrow of soul was theirs,
and mood of mourning. The King himself labored in woe for
loss of his lordly athelings. Gigantic footsteps they found; and
far to a lone mountain-tarn they traced the trail of the foe; yet
no longer than after one night, Grendel again returning, wrought
ruthless murder more grievous. Too old to meet Grendel was
Hrothgar; but oft as his beer they drank, boasted his warsmen to
bide in the beer-hall and meet this grim Grendel with sword-
blades. Then was the mead-house at morn dyed with blood;
Hrothgar had heroes the less, doughty dear-ones that death had
reft. At last all the athelings feared to sleep in the Hall of Horrors;
they sought rest in buildings apart. Empty and idle the mead-
hall as soon as the evening sun in the harbor of heaven was hid.

Thus had Grendel mastery, and warred against the right, he
alone against all. A great while it was, twelve winters that the
King endured this woe. The evil one ambushed young and old,
dark death-shadow dogging his prey, luring them, lurking the
livelong night in mists of the moorland. O'er Heorot he lorded,
gold-bright hall, in gloomy nights; and ne'er could the King
approach his throne or have joy in his hall. Many warsmen,
assembled, sought counsel how bold-hearted men this horror
could help, the whiles they vowed altar-offerings within their
heathen fanes; yet still, without ceasing, Hrothgar brooded his
season of sorrow, sad and despairing of succor.

And now began gleemen to sing the sorrowful song abroad
how Grendel strove against Hrothgar. So it befell that Be'o-wulf,
born a thane of the Geat-folk, heard tell of this tale of terror.
Strongest in might of manhood in that same day of this our
life, stalwart and stately was Beowulf, having in his hand-grip
thirty men's heft of grasp! For high-hearted valor, Beowulf
donned his war-weeds, ancient and mystic armor, woven-work of

FROM THE TOWER WINDOW

Wayland, weapon-smith to the gods; and he bade be fitted a good sea-goer that he might fare over the swan-road, over the sea-streets, Hrothgar to help in his horror. Picked warriors of the Geat-folk, the boldest, Beowulf chose; and sped by the wind, their bark, like a bird with breast of foam, glided over the waters. At sunrise, the seafarers saw the shore-cliffs gleaming before them. They sprang to the beach and thanked God for their passage in peace o'er the whale-path.

Now saw from a cliff the warden that watched the waterside, how they bore over the gangway glittering shields and wargear, and how the golden boars gleamed grimly on their helmets. Wonder seized him to know what manner of men they were. "Who are ye in battle-gear," he cried, "leading a deep-ship hither?"

Beowulf made answer: "To Hrothgar I would bring succor, that his boiling care-waves may cool!"

So the warden guided the Geat-folk till Heorot they saw, broad of gable and bright with gold; the hall that was among earth-dwellers famed beyond all halls under heaven,—the sheen of it flashed afar. Stone-bright the street led on, showing the way to the clansmen. Then hied that troop where the herald led them under Heorot's roof. The hero strode, hardy 'neath helm, to the hearth in the midst of the hall. On the high-seat, white-haired and old, surrounded by earls, sat Hrothgar; and unto him, unto Hrothgar, Beowulf unrestrained, now unlocked his word-hoard: "O Prince of the Bright Danes, guardian of warriors, beloved friend of the people, I beg to destroy this demon! His charms render weapons powerless. No sword will I use against him. With hand-grip alone grasp I Grendel!"

"Sore is my soul," said Hrothgar, "to say to any of the race of man what ruth for me in Heorot Grendel with hate hath wrought, —what sudden harryings. Hall-folk fail, my warriors wane; but God is able this deadly foe from his deeds to turn. Now sit to the banquet. I beg thee unbind thy words, hardy hero, as heart shall prompt thee."

Then Geatish men gathered together, their benches and tressle-tables running the length of both walls, while haughty at end of the hall Hrothgar sat on his high-seat; and opposite Hroth-gar, Beowulf. A henchman with carven cup, poured out the shining mead, and oft the minstrels sang blithe. In Heorot heroes revelled with laughter of liege-men loud. Came Weal'theow, Queen of Hrothgar, gold-decked, greeting the guests, handing to all the mead-cup, till came the moment when ring-graced, she bore the beaker to Beowulf. Greeting the lord of the Geats, God she thanked that here was a hero on whom her hope could lean. The cup he took, hardy-in-war, and thus answered, eager for combat, "Either I will do deeds that free your people wholly, or fighting fall to the foe, fast in the fist of the fiend!"

Pleased with his battle-boast, the stately dame, bright with gold, sat down by her spouse on the high-seat. Again the proud bands revelled, but Hrothgar knew well that the fiend purposed fight when the sheen of the sun should vanish, when dusk of the night sank darkling, and shadowy shapes came striding, stalking 'neath the sky. So Hrothgar led forth his hero-train, and Beowulf, with his battle-braves, bided alone in the place. Baring bench-boards of trenchers and mead-cups, spreading bolsters and beds on the benches, each atheling hung over his head his helmet, corselet, and spear; for so 'twas the custom of heroes to sleep in the hall of wassail. Spake then his vaunt, bold Beowulf: "With hand-grip alone grasp I Grendel; and let the wise God decree doom on which side he deemeth right!"

Brave for battle, he mounted his bed; while his men on their hall-beds sank. None of them thought that thence their steps to the folk that fostered them, to the land they loved would lead back. Well they wist, that on warriors many would battle-death seize that night.

Through wan night came striding the stalker - in - shadow. From moorland, by misty crags, with God's wrath laden, came Grendel! Under the clouds he came, till the mead-hall, the gold-hall, he saw, gleaming and flashing with fretwork. The portal he found fast bolted. Baleful in blatant rage, he burst the house's mouth. O'er the fair-paved floor he trod on, ireful, his eyes flashing flame! He spied in the hall the heroes, kin and clansmen clustered asleep. Then his heart laughed for joy of the banquet lying in wait to his will. A sleeping warrior he seized, and tore him fiercely asunder. For Beowulf, hardy hero, with fiendish claw he grasped. But the hero, reclining, was watching; he clutched the fiend's claw boldly. Soon saw that shepherd-of-evils that never he met in this mid-world, in all the ways of earth, a wight with heavier hand-grip. Fain would he flee, his fastness seek, the den of devils; but Beowulf grasped him firm nor could the fiend free his fist. Din filled the room; there crashed from the sill many mead-benches. Wonder it was that the wine-hall stood firm in the strain of their struggle.

Danes, filled with fear and frenzy, heard Grendel wailing his out-cry, God's foe sounding stave of terror, his grisly song of defeat. Now Beowulf's earls awakening, brandished blades to shield their lord; but no keenest blade ever fashioned could hurt that hideous fiend. Him Beowulf held with his hand till Grendel took mortal hurt. A mighty wound showed on his shoulder; sinews cracked; the bone-frame burst; and Beowulf dragged from the socket shoulder, arm, and claw! Thence Grendel, death-sick, his den in the dark moor sought; knowing well that here was the last of life, an end of his days on earth. To Eastern Danes had the valiant Geat his vaunt made good. As proof he hung Grendel's claw beneath the roof of Heorot.

Many at morning the men who gathered the wonder to witness; folk-leaders faring from far and near, the tracks of the foe did trace, how, worsted in fight, he fled to die in the mere of the monsters. Then home rode the hoary clansmen, while youths set their white steeds to race whenever the road seemed fair; and from time to time a thane of the King, mindful of ancient sagas, bound word to word in well-knit rhyme, welding song of Beowulf's glory. The King and the Queen with her maidens, measured the path to the Mead-house. Hrothgar stood by the steps and saw Grendel's claw 'neath the roof. "God still works wonder on wonder, the Warden-of-Glory," he cried.

Then was hurry and haste in Heorot for hands to bedeck it; and dense was the throng of men and women the wine-hall to cleanse. Gold-gay shone the woven hangings that garnished the walls. To hall then proceeded Beowulf. The King himself sat to the banquet. To Beowulf, Hrothgar gave a banner woven of gold, a breast-plate, a helmet, and sword; then he bade lead adown the hall eight steeds with carven head-gear, whereof one was duly decked with splendid jeweled saddle, the battle-seat of the best of kings, when in his younger days he fared forth to the sword-play. To Geatish earls, too, he gave gifts, and the

FROM THE TOWER WINDOW

Queen-under-gold-crown, Wealtheow, with winsome words, and with gifts, likewise rewarded Beowulf. That was the proudest of feasts; harping was heard with the hero-lay, as Hrothgar's singers woke hall-joy all along the mead-seats; but when the evening was come, homeward Hrothgar did hasten, royal to his rest. Beowulf, too, left the hall, bound for a bed apart. The earls, left to guard the mead-hall, spread their beds on the benches, and sank secure to their slumber, deeming all danger was done.

But since that grim fight, Grendel's mother, a monster-wife, mourned her woe, dwelling in dark, dreary waters. Gloomy and grim, she came on a quest her son to avenge. Into the hall-house she burst, the mother of Grendel. He, who for Hrothgar of heroes was dearest, she killed on his couch. Uproar filled Heorot. Grendel's arm she tore down, and fled in haste to the moorlands.

For Hrothgar a steed was saddled, a steed with plaited mane. Then Hrothgar bade Beowulf come and with him seek out Grendel's mother. They followed the monster's foot-prints over the murky moors. They followed o'er beetling cliffs, fearful fenways and narrow passes, sheer headlands and haunts of the Nicors. So they came to a mountain forest, dank and foul, the woeful wood, and beneath it, black, boiling waters, waters dyed with blood, and, wonder weird to see, fearful fire on the waters! And there crawled worm-like things, sea-dragons and savage Nicors, such as oft on the road-of-sails pursue ruthless quest of sailors.

Then Beowulf leapt in the flood. An hour of the day fled by, and many a monster he met—sea-beasts swarming upon him, tearing his mail with fierce tusks, ere he felt the floor of the sea. Then lo! a great claw grasped him and dragged him down to a fearsome hall, whither no water entered. There Beowulf faced Grendel's mother, wolf-of-the-deep, mere-wife monstrous. His good blade he swung for a blow. On her head sang its war-song wild; but useless was Beowulf's sword against charms of the she-one.

He cast it aside, strong and steel-edged, and trusted once more

to his hand-grip. With grisly grasp Grendel's mother grappled with Beowulf, till spent with the struggle, the fighter on foot, strongest of warriors, stumbled. The water-wife hurled herself on him; her dagger drew, broad and bright-edged. So had life ended for Beowulf, had not Holy God, the Wise Lord, held sway over the victory, awarding it aright. Midst the war-gear on the cave's walls, Beowulf saw of a sudden, an old sword of the giants, glory of warriors and choicest of weapons, save greater than any man else might think to bear to the battle. Beowulf seized it, and, battle-grim, smiting, slew Grendel's mother.

Steadfast of thought, the hero looked through the under-sea cave-hall, and finding where Grendel lay dead, he bore off his head to Hrothgar. Then up through the waters he dove. Safely he swam to the land. Hrothgar had gone home to Heorot; but Beowulf's chosen band had long sat sick at heart, watching the sad sea surges, fearful for his returning. God they thanked to see him again. Then forth they fared by the foot-path, four bearing Grendel's head. So to the palace they came. Said Beowulf: "Lord of the Scyldings, sleep safely henceforth in Heorot!"

Joyful of heart was Hrothgar; he gave treasures twelve to the hero, while all men averred that from sea to sea there was none under vault of heaven more valiant than Beowulf! Their ocean-keel boarding, the Geat-men dove again through the deep; and foam-flecked their vessel floated, till they sighted the cliffs of home.

FROM THE TOWER WINDOW

Lohengrin*

RETOLD FROM THE OPERA BY RICHARD WAGNER

OF OLD times in Flanders, the duchy of Brabant boasted many castles, crowning the tree-covered hillsides or rising from flowery meadows along the River Scheldt. Now it chanced in this duchy that strife and trouble arose. Years before, the Duke of Brabant had died leaving his small son, Godfrey, as heir to the duchy. When the Duke was on his deathbed, he had called to his side the most trusted of his friends, Frederick of Telramund. "My friend," the Duke then said, "for the love I bear to you, I leave in your care my most precious treasure, my motherless children, Elsa and Godfrey. Be their guardian until they are grown."

So, when the good Duke died, the children went to live at the castle of Telramund. Elsa, the elder of the two, grew to be a beautiful maid and she and the young boy, Godfrey, often disported themselves by tramping together in the woods which covered the hill below the castle. But one day Godfrey, adventuring, wandered far away from his sister and did not come back again. She sought for him everywhere, but could not find a single trace of him. Pale and trembling with grief, she returned at length to the castle to report that he was lost. Peasants, servants, knights hunted for days and weeks, but Godfrey could not be found.

Then Ortrud, the wife of Telramund, an ambitious and wicked woman, seeing the heir to the duchy conveniently out of the way, thought this an opportunity for her husband to discredit Elsa, the next heir to the duchy, and make himself Duke of Brabant. So she whispered in his ear that, if he would but accuse Elsa of having killed her brother, he would do away with her easily and safely reign in her stead. Telramund was persuaded. He made the accusation, whereupon there arose such confusion and strife in

*Lohengrin is one of Wagner's most popular operas. Wagner discovered the old Germanic epic one summer and took it to the woods, where, stretched beside a brook, he recreated in fancy the world of the old legend.

Brabant that King Henry of Germany, overlord of the country, came in haste to Antwerp to give judgment in the case.

Surrounded by the counts and nobles of Saxony and Brabant, the King sat under the Oak of Justice and called on Frederick of Telramund, a knight whom he greatly trusted, to lay the matter before him.

"Most gracious King," cried Telramund, "I here accuse the Princess Elsa of having killed her brother. Alone those two went to the woods and no man has seen the boy since! Give judgment, O King, against her!"

Much disturbed, the King asked that Elsa be brought before him. Timid, with downcast eyes, the girl came into his presence.

"Speak, Elsa," said the King. "In me, thou mayest confide."

But the young girl seemed bewildered at the enormity of the crime of which she had been accused, for she had loved Godfrey dearly. No word could she speak in her own defence. She could only tell of the long lonely hours when, in the depths of her trouble, she had prayed heaven for help. "But while I lay asleep," she cried, "I saw in splendor shining a knight of glorious mien, who turned his tranquil gaze on me and spoke words low and tender that brought new life to me." Her voice rose into rapture as she recalled her dream. "My guardian, my defender, my champion that knight shall be!"

Moved deeply, King Henry hearkened. Then, after the fashion of the time, he decreed that the question of Elsa's guilt or innocence should be left to a trial of arms, if any knight should appear to fight with Telramund in behalf of the unhappy princess. Trumpeters blew the summons North, South, East, and West and the herald called aloud:

"Who will do battle here for Elsa of Brabant?"

At first there came no response. Elsa fell on her knees in prayer. "See, she is guilty!" cried Telramund. But again the trumpeters blew their summons North, South, East, and West.

Elsa, in the opera, bewildered by the charges of murdering her brother, answers them only by relating her vision of a splendid knight who came to be her defender. This beautiful soprano aria is called *Elsa's Dream*.

FROM THE TOWER WINDOW

At that a strange sight appeared. Round the distant bend of the river came gliding a beautiful boat drawn by a snow-white swan. In the boat stood a knight, his silver armor gleaming, his shield and sword of gold. He was the Knight of Elsa's dream. Breathless, the people looked on as the boat drew in to the shore and the Knight stepped out on the bank. Stroking the swan's white neck, the Knight said tenderly:

"I give thee thanks, my faithful swan!
Turn again and breast the tide,
Return unto that land of dawn,
Where, joyous, we did long abide.
Well thy appointed task is done!
Farewell, farewell, my trusty swan!"

Whenever the swan appears in the opera, there is a beautiful swan theme. The music glides and undulates like a swan on the water and makes one feel the mystery, sadness, and tenderness associated with the swan.

As the graceful bird glided away, the Knight turned to the King.

"Hail, gracious sovereign," he cried. "I am come to defend the Princess Elsa of Brabant. Guiltless and true is she and false is Count Telramund!"

Elsa was in rapture and Telramund in a rage. In the center of a circle of people, the two knights faced each other. The King then offered a prayer that God should judge between them and give victory to the innocent.

"Now Lord, make known Thy just decree! I have no fear. I trust in Thee!" cried Elsa. But Ortrud looked at her husband.

"In his strong arm, I trust alone," she said, "that no defeat nor fear hath known!"

Three times the King struck his sword with resounding blow against his shield which hung on the Oak of Justice. With drawn swords, Telramund and Elsa's mysterious champion rushed at one another. But the struggle was soon over. The Knight, with one swift blow, struck Telramund to the ground. He spared his life, however, and helped him to his feet. Then, while Ortrud and Telramund slipped away in disgrace, the people hailed with praise the shining Knight of the Swan. Going to Elsa, the stranger begged her to plight troth with him, but, on no condition, to ask until a year had passed who he was or whence he came. Joyously Elsa promised and put her hand in his.

That night Telramund sat, ashamed and in somber garments, with Ortrud on the church steps. Chagrined, he blamed his wife for all that had occurred.

"Once I was respected by all the people," he wailed. "Now I have lost my knighthood and must hide myself in shame!"

But Ortrud comforted him. "Tonight," she whispered, "I read in the stars a secret. If this mysterious knight can be made to tell his name, all his power will end. I shall pretend to be Elsa's friend, then slyly arouse her suspicions till she demands to know his name."

The King, in the opera, calls on Heaven to judge between the Knight and Telramund in a great aria called the *King's Prayer* which begins "Oh, King of Kings, on Thee I call."

FROM THE TOWER WINDOW

Just then Elsa appeared on a balcony above them. All unconscious of the two hiding in the shadows below, the girl, in a blissful reverie, sang to the wandering breezes of her love for the shining Knight to whom she was now betrothed.

"Trust in me," said Ortrud to her husband. "I shall have revenge." Then drawing her black shawl over her head, she approached Elsa humbly. "Have pity on me and on my poor husband," she pleaded. "We are both sorry for what we have done and seek your pardon, dear maid."

Rapturous in her new happiness, Elsa came down from the balcony to cheer the sorrowing Ortrud. "Do not grieve," she said and put her arm over Ortrud's shoulders. "Weep no more, my dear, but come to my wedding tomorrow. Come and rejoice with me."

"Thy friend, sweet maid," said Ortrud, "I shall always be, but let me beg thee, since thy happiness is very dear to me, not to trust too blindly this knight whom thou knowest so little. He may leave thee as mysteriously as he appeared to thine aid. Remember, dearest Elsa, thou knowest not even his name."

"Nay," said Elsa gently, "with love there cometh trust." But Ortrud rejoiced in secret that she had planted a seed of suspicion in Elsa's heart.

When morning dawned, nobles and country folk thronged to the castle square for the festivities of the wedding. When many were assembled, the herald of the King stepped forth and announced that Telramund had been pronounced a traitor and banished from the land. The mysterious Knight of the Swan, who would that day become the husband of Princess Elsa, was to reign in Brabant.

"All hail the Duke of Brabant!" the people shouted and cheered. Then they crowded toward the church to await the coming of the bride. Dressed in long, white robes, Elsa at length appeared, accompanied by her bridesmaids. Then, suddenly,

Ortrud swept forth in splendid garments again. Imperiously lifting her hand, she cried out angrily, "Stop!"

Overcome at this change in one who had begged her friendship only the night before, Elsa asked in astonishment: "Ortrud, what does this mean?"

"My husband has been tricked by a stranger whom no one knows," cried Ortrud. "You are his bride-to-be, yet you cannot even speak his name!"

"Slanderer! Taunt me no more!" cried Elsa. "My knight is pure and noble!"

Just then the Knight, himself, came into the square with the King. Seeing Ortrud present, he stepped to Elsa's side.

"Why is this evil one present?" he cried.

"Last night, I found her weeping and cheered her with my compassion," Elsa replied. "Yet today, with harsh words of hatred, she comes to taunt me for my boundless trust in thee."

"Begone!" said the Knight to Ortrud and again the bridal party started for the church. But Telramund now rushed forth.

"Hear, King and nobles," he cried, "this stranger is a sorcerer, not worthy to be a knight. Only through black magic could he be guided by a swan! And think you, he refuses to tell his name and country!"

"That will I tell to no earthly prince," cried the Knight.

"Say no more!" the King cried to Telramund, but Telramund whispered in Elsa's ear: "You do not know his name. Doubt him." Then the party entered the church.

When the ceremony was over, the people, led by pages with lighted torches, escorted the bride and groom, to the strains of a glorious wedding march, back to their rooms in the castle. There, voicing every good wish, they left the two alone.

But now in the heart of Elsa, the taunts of Ortrud and Telramund had done their deadly work. All at once she broke her

The triumphant wedding march, played after the wedding of Elsa and the Knight, has become the traditional march for a wedding procession, followed by the "Wedding March" from Mendelssohn's fairy opera, *Midsummer Night's Dream*. See Vol. VI, page 61.

vow and asked the fatal question. "Husband, tell me your name."

"Elsa!" cried the Knight in anguish. "Remember the vow you made!"

"Tell me," coaxed Elsa prettily, "where no one else can hear."

"Dearest, remember your promise!"

Again and again she begged. "I shall keep it a secret," she vowed.

"Elsa! Elsa! You know not what you do!" cried the Knight.

Then even as she begged, the door was burst suddenly open and Telramund appeared, followed by four of his men. Drawing their swords, they rushed, all five, at the stranger Knight. Elsa rose with a shriek and handed her husband his sword. One stroke and he killed Telramund! Then Telramund's four followers fell on their knees before him, while Elsa dropped fainting in his arms. For a long time the Knight stood silent, but at last, he gave Elsa over to be cared for by her ladies.

"All my joys are fled," he cried. "Tell Elsa that tomorrow, before the King and his nobles, I shall tell my name and whence it was I came."

The next morning the army assembled along the bank of the river, awaiting their commander, the new Duke of Brabant. There, too, was the King with whom the Duke of Brabant was about to set forth to battle. But the Duke was slow to appear. Four knights came, instead, with the body of Telramund, and after them came Elsa, her eyes cast down and sad as she leaned for support on one of her ladies. At last came the Knight, himself. A cheer went up to greet him, but he stepped before the King.

"Gracious sovereign," he cried, "I beg you find me blameless for slaying this man who sought my life."

"Aye," the King declared, "the man was justly slain."

"And further," said the Knight, "I shall not lead these men to battle. Bitter grief is mine; for that dear bride, whom Heaven gave me, hath been driven from her allegiance. Ye all have heard her vow she would not ask my name and country. Yet her impatient heart hath broken the vow she made."

"Woe is thine, Elsa!" cried the women.

"Oh, what hast thou done?" cried the men.

"I will no more withhold my secret," said the Knight. "In a far distant land, there lies a mount called Montsalvat, which holds a shrine most precious. Within that shrine, all throned in light, there stands the Holy Grail, that cup immortal from which our Savior drank at his Last Supper. 'Twas borne by angels to the earth, and whoso looks on it is cleansed of sin and pure of heart. Once every year, a dove descends from Heaven to strengthen it anew for works of grace, and all the power of Heaven attends those faithful knights who guard the place. Aye, he who serves the Grail is armed henceforth with might invincible to conquer evil; nor will he lose the charm it lendeth, though he go to distant lands to fight in some good cause. While his name's unknown, he still commands its spell; but, once he's known, he must depart and flee. The Grail it was that sent me here to right yon lady's wrong. My father, Percival, reigns gloriously on Montsalvat. His knight am I. My name is Lohengrin."

As Lohengrin ceased speaking, some one cried, "The holy tears run down my cheek at hearing of his tale!"

And Elsa moaned, " 'Tis dark around me! Give me air! Oh, help! Oh, me, most wretched!"

There fell a hush upon the crowd. Then one in great excitement cried, "The swan! The swan! The swan! He's floating down the stream! The swan! He comes!"

Half-fainting, Elsa moaned again, "Oh, horror! Ah, the swan!"

Sadly Lohengrin then bade his wife farewell.

"Oh, Elsa, think what joys your doubts have ended. Could you not have trusted me for only one short year? Then would I have been free to tell you all my secret."

FROM THE TOWER WINDOW

Taking his horn and sword, Lohengrin gave them to Elsa. "Should your brother, Godfrey, return, give him these!" he said. "If ever on the battlefield, he finds himself in need, bid him blow this horn and tell him that, with my sacred sword, he can conquer every foe. And now farewell, my love! I return to Montsalvat: there to remain forever, a knight of the Holy Grail."

With drooping spirit and heavy heart, he walked toward the bank of the river, once again greeting with tenderness his trusty friend, the Swan. But, as he turned away, Ortrud rushed into the crowd. "Aha! my magic art is supreme!" she boasted gleefully. "I bewitched Godfrey by placing a gold band about his neck! He is none other than that swan! See, the band still encircles his throat!"

Furiously, the people cursed her for a witch and threatened to burn her to death. But Lohengrin fell to his knees and offered up a prayer. In answer, a great white dove, the dove of the Holy Grail, came floating down from the clouds and hovered over the skiff. Then Lohengrin loosed the band around the neck of the swan. Behold! The swan sank from sight and out of the water Lohengrin lifted a prince in shining armor. "Behold!" he cried to the people. "Behold the Duke of Brabant!"

In a fury of rage at the sight, Ortrud fell to the ground.

"All hail, Godfrey, Duke of Brabant!" the soldiers shouted while Elsa clasped her brother in her arms.

But, when the crowd had recovered from its moment's surprise and interest in Godfrey's return, they looked around for Lohengrin. Lo, the dove of the Holy Grail was guiding the boat up the river off toward Montsalvat, and in it stood Lohengrin, his head sunk on his breast as he sadly leaned on his shield. Silent, the people watched the boat pass around the bend of the river; but, when it disappeared, they broke out into weeping. Elsa sank almost lifeless into her brother's arms. "Lohengrin!" she called. "Lohengrin!" But Lohengrin was gone and he would never return.

Joan of Arc

the year 1412, there was born in the village of Dom-re-my′ in France, a little peasant girl called Joan of Arc. Her parents were honest laboring folk and they lived in a cottage that bordered directly on the churchyard. In the cool and peaceful shadow of the church with all its holy associations, Joan spent with her brothers and sisters a very happy childhood. She shared with unbounded energy all their joyous activity and sports, yet who so ready as she to perform her share of the household tasks or respond to any command of her parents with simple loving obedience? Beneath the stately trees of the splendid old forest of Domremy, she tended her father's sheep and she aided him too in many a rough man's task, yet in heart and soul she was every whit a woman, thoroughly skilled in fine needlework and all womanly household arts. Every one in the village loved Joan for the charm of her sweet simplicity and her wholly unselfish kindness. Deep in the heart of the girl was implanted an earnest love of God as well as a love of her fellow men, and as she grew somewhat older she often went apart from the boisterous play of the other children to pass many hours in quiet meditation and prayer, her thoughts sweeping out far beyond the little circle of daily concerns that occupied her playmates.

Now the affairs of France were at this time in a most unhappy state. For the English in league with the Burgundians, had conquered almost the whole of France, and the Dauphin Charles VII, having never the courage to get himself crowned, was looking on in lazy indolence without a thought of resistance, even meditating flight and the total abandonment of his kingdom,—a sorry king with no money, no army and, worst of all, no spirit and no purpose.

Over all these things Joan pondered with the most serious

Jeanne d'Arc, the opera by Tchaikovsky, tells the story of Joan's life. "Farewell, My Forests" is a famous aria sung by Joan.

concern, and her deep-rooted conviction of the goodness and power of God, her live consciousness of God as a very real presence, filled her with the most certain assurance that naught so unjust as the forceful conquest of France by alien invaders could ever be accomplished. All the power and strength and might of God were against such injustice. In her heart and soul strange stirrings and longings awoke till at length all her waking hours were spent in almost continuous prayer for her country's deliverance.

One summer's day when Joan was thirteen years old she was wandering alone in her father's garden at midday, her spirit more than ever astir within her, when she suddenly heard a voice call her. Instantly a great light shone upon her and she saw the archangel Michael before her. He bade her continue to be a good girl and made the solemn announcement that it was she and none other who should save the kingdom of France, who should go to the help of the Dauphin and bring him to Rheims to be crowned. The child, so young and weak before such a mighty task, fell on her knees overcome. "I am but a poor girl," she said.

"God will help thee," answered the angel.

From this day Joan's life became even more pure and sweet than before. She loved to go apart from her playmates and meditate, and now heavenly voices often spoke to her telling her of her mission. These she said were the voices of her saints. Sometimes the voices were accompanied by visions. St. Catherine and St. Margaret appeared to her. Thus the child grew to young maidenhood, her mind elevated by her visions.

At the beginning of the year 1428, when Joan was sixteen, the Voices told her that the time was now come when she could no longer delay. She must go at once to the Dauphin to save the kingdom. They commanded her first to seek out the Sire de Baudricourt (Bo'dri-coor) and ask of him an escort to conduct her to the Dauphin. Conscious that her parents, bound by their fearful human love for her, would never aid her in such an undertaking, Joan went to an uncle and begged him to accompany her to the Sire at Vaucouleurs (Vo-coo-leur'). Her ardent sincerity overcame the objections of the peasant and he went with her.

Baudricourt's reception of Joan was brutal. When the girl told him that she was destined of God to lead the Dauphin to his coronation, and begged him to send her to Charles, he cried: "The girl is crazy! Box her ears and take her back to her father."

Thus Joan was returned with scorn to Domremy. Another less earnest and consecrated, might have been shamed by such a reception into yielding up her purpose. But urged by her Voices, Joan persisted and went once more to Baudricourt. He received her with the same mocking disbelief as before.

Soon nothing was talked of at Vaucouleurs but the young girl who went about openly saying that God destined her to save the kingdom and some one must take her to Charles the Dauphin. At length while the Sire and his noble friends utterly scoffed at the idea that God should give a poor peasant girl power to save a kingdom where the most experienced generals had failed, the simple-hearted people, moved by her faith, began to believe in her mission. A certain young squire offered to take her to Chi-non' where Charles was then staying. The poor folk, heaping all their little savings together, raised money enough to clothe and arm her and buy her a horse. Thus with a small escort she set out for Chinon. Baudricourt still flung his jibes after her, but the multitude, many among them weeping to see the young thing go so bravely forth to face such fearful odds, cried from the very depths of their hearts, "God keep you!"

English and Burgundians held all the country over which the little party must pass and every bridge was occupied by the enemy. Thus Joan had to travel by night and hide by day. Her companions soon began to lose heart in the face of such dangers and urge a return to Vaucouleurs, but Joan's answer was resolute; "Fear nothing, for God is leading me."

FROM THE TOWER WINDOW

On the twelfth day after starting, the party arrived at Chinon.

Now the courtiers of Charles VII were by no means agreed as to how this maiden who made such remarkable claims should be received. Some, jealous of their power over the mind of the Dauphin, urged him not to receive her at all. But just at that moment came news from Orleans, almost the last great French stronghold to hold out against the English, that it was like to fall, and those courtiers who favored Joan carried their point that the last chance of saving Orleans should not be neglected.

By the flaring light of torches, Joan was led one evening to the castle. She had never seen the King and the great hall was crowded with nobles. In order to test the truth of the girl's claim that she was inspired of God, the Dauphin had attired himself in a plain costume and stood in the midst of a throng of his nobles while one of his courtiers in the royal robes sat upon the throne. Joan however did not hesitate. She singled Charles out at a glance, came at once and knelt before him.

"I am not the King," he asserted. "Yonder is the King."

"You are he, gentle Prince and no other," the girl insisted.

And then she proceeded to tell the Dauphin of her mission, assuring him with all the fire of her high and noble purpose burning in her eyes, that God had sent her to have him crowned and save the kingdom of France. Still the young coward hesitated. He was afraid that the girl might be a sorceress, so he sent her off to be examined by a body of learned men and ecclesiastics. For three weeks these men tormented her with questions, but she answered them always straight to the point and in face of all their suspicions and efforts to entrap her, her inspiration and self-command never once flagged or failed.

"If it be God's intent to save France, He hath no need of men-at-arms to accomplish His purpose," objected the tribunal.

"The soldiers must do the fighting, but God will give the victory," Joan quietly made answer.

At length the common people once again declared in favor of the girl and the learned and powerful were forced to yield to the simple faith of the multitude. The troops gathered at Blois and Joan arrived there followed by the greatest nobles of France. She rode in armor and on horse-back, an appealing girlish figure of a natural grace and dignity that softened and subdued even the rudest of the soldiers. She bore a white banner of her own design which was intended to remind the army continually of the purity of their cause and the God who was their strength.

Dunois who was in command at Orleans, came to meet Joan. She said to him simply, "I bring you the best of help, that of the King of Heaven. It comes not from me but from God Himself."

At eight in the evening Joan entered Orleans. The people crowded to meet her. In the midst of a throng so dense that she could scarcely make her way, she passed by torchlight through the city. Men, women and children wished to get near her and even to touch her horse. Joan spoke to them with compassion and promised to deliver them. First of all she asked to be led to a church to offer thanks to God. As she passed along the way, an old man cried out to her, "My daughter, the English are strong and well intrenched. It will be difficult to get rid of them!" She answered confidently, "Nothing is impossible to God."

Her confidence infected everyone around her. The people of Orleans so lately timid and discouraged, wished now to throw themselves at once upon the enemy. But Dunois, fearful of defeat, decided to await reinforcements which Charles had promised to send to Joan from Blois. In the meantime from the walls of Orleans, Joan summoned the English to depart and return to their own country, but they answered her with insults. The reinforcements from Blois were so long in appearing that Dunois at length went himself to see what had become of them. He arrived just in time to discover that the weak and changeable Dauphin had been influenced by jealous courtiers to desert Joan

and send the troops not to her but back to their quarters. With difficulty Dunois prevailed on Charles to send the men to Orleans.

On the fourth of May the battle began. Everywhere, Joan was in the thick of the fight, urging on her men without a thought of herself. But never did she use her sword; her standard was her sole weapon. Once while she was taking a little rest, the commander, without her knowledge, ordered an attack on a certain bastion held by the English. Always the commanders were jealously attempting to gain the victory without Joan in order to take to themselves the credit. But their attack failed and the French were retreating in great disorder when Joan awakened suddenly from her sleep and rushed up to their assistance. She rallied them and led them once more against the foe. This time the English strove in vain to maintain their position. They were forced to surrender the bastion. Thus Joan was led in great glory back to Orleans, but as she crossed the battlefield where in the heat of contest her determined spirit had upheld them all, she gave way and wept like any woman for compassion of the wounds and suffering that had been caused by the battle.

It was now a question how to follow up against the English this attack so happily begun. The leaders, far from pleased to be led by a peasant girl and to share with her the victory, met in secret to discuss the plans to be adopted. Joan presented herself indignantly at the council, and as the chancellor of the Duke of Orleans tried to conceal the decisions which had been made, she cried, "Tell me what you have concluded. You have been at your council and I at mine!"—she meant that she had been earnestly at prayer,—"and believe me, the counsels of God shall be accomplished and stand while yours shall perish!"

Thereafter she did indeed lead the French to most brilliant victory. Often she angered the generals by not taking their advice and pursuing the most approved military tactics, but she lent to the men a spirited resolution and inspired them with boundless faith. Moreover she herself was so persuaded that victory was inevitable if she persevered unflinchingly in her efforts to obtain it, that nothing could stand before her. So in four days the English, who had been for eight months before Orleans, were forced to give up the siege.

News of the victory spread far and wide and attested in the sight of all the truth of Joan's assertion that she was led of God. The holy maid did not linger to be praised and thanked by the people of Orleans, but returned hastily to Chinon, desiring to take Charles at once to Rheims to be crowned. But the Dauphin though he received her with great honors, refused to follow her to Rheims, not intending that she should disturb the base indolence of his royal existence. Accordingly Joan proceeded against the English again, and won three more great battles, driving the foe beyond the Loire. Then at last, still reluctantly, Charles was induced to surrender his ease long enough to go to Rheims. On the sixteenth of July, he entered the city at the head of his troops and the next day the ceremony of coronation took place in the cathedral before a great concourse of people. When Charles had been crowned, Joan flung herself at his feet weeping hot tears.

"O Sire," she cried, "Now is accomplished the will of God!"

"All who saw her at the moment," says the old chronicle, "believed more than ever that it was a thing come from God," and the attachment of the common people to her was a touching sight. They contested among themselves to kiss her hands or her clothes or only to touch her. It was the moment of her supremest triumph. And now that Joan had fulfilled all her mission, obeyed all the commands that God had given her, she earnestly besought Charles to let her return to her home to the sweet simplicity of her early life, for in all she had done she had no smallest thought of reward or self-glorification, but only of simple devotion to God and to France. The Dauphin however would not now let her go. He commanded her to remain at the head of his army. At this a great indecision came upon Joan. Against her judgment she obeyed him, and from the moment of her yielding to his will, instead of to her own inner counsellors, her Voices deserted her; her inspiration fled. Her path from now on was the sad downward path of defeat.

Joan wished to proceed at once against Paris, but the King hesitated and so gave the English time to prepare their defense. When the assault at last was made, it was repulsed, and Joan was severely wounded. Yet they had to drag her away from the foot of the ramparts to make her abandon the conflict. The next day the King utterly refused to renew the attack though Joan answered for its success. He was not willing to exert himself any further; he must resume his indolent ease. Therefore he stubbornly insisted on a retreat. With a heart full of grief, Joan followed the King. It was her first defeat and it instantly dispelled the implicit faith of the people in her. One sent of God they argued could never be defeated. Little they knew that since the coronation at Rheims it had been the King's will and not the inspiration of God to which Joan had been obedient. Thinking there had been enough of fighting and wishing to put a stop to Joan's successes, the courtiers induced Charles to disband his army and give up all further activity against the invaders. A sad situation for Joan. Taking unceremonious leave of the King, she went to help the French wherever they were still fighting.

At length, after many adventures, Joan came to Compiègne to lead the garrison out against the Burgundians who pressed them hard, but the English came to the aid of the Burgundians and the French gave back, carrying Joan unwillingly with them in the midst of their retreat. When she and her party came under the walls of Compiègne, they found the gates closed. The commander of the city whom Joan had come to succor, had deliberately shut her out from the shelter of its walls. With her back against the bank of the moat, Joan still defended herself till a whole troop rushed upon her. Nor did she ever surrender but was dragged by her flowing garments from her horse and taken prisoner. From the walls of the city the governor saw her taken but raised not a finger to save her.

So Joan fell into the hands of her bitter enemies who hated her for her successes against them, and after a few months, the Burgundians sold her to the English. All this time, Charles whom she had made King of France, never offered to ransom her, nor

FROM THE TOWER WINDOW

from now on through her time of trial showed the slightest interest in her. Shut up in the dungeon of the Castle at Rouen, she was guarded day and night by soldiers whose brutality and insults she was forced to endure. But now to her joy her Voices came back to console and support her. Once more she had the unspeakable comfort of knowing that God was with her.

At length she was given over to the inquisition for trial. To the insidious questions of her judges the unhappy maiden had nothing to oppose but the uprightness and simplicity of her heart.

"Take good heed what you do," she said, "for truly I am sent by God and you put yourselves in great peril."

She was nevertheless condemned as a heretic and sorceress and ordered to be burnt at the stake in the market place at Rouen. On the thirtieth of May, 1431, she was led to the place of execution. At the foot of the pile, she asked for a cross, and she died with the name of Jesus on her lips, her eyes bright as with triumph and her whole face transfigured with the consolation of hearkening to her Voices. All were weeping, even the executioners and judges, and a great fear came upon all.

The Story of the Cid*

A Spanish Epic, retold from the ancient Poem of the Cid

IN days long gone, great throngs of dark-skinned Moors came swarming from the shores of Africa across Gibraltar's narrow strait to over-run fair Spain. And then behold strong Moorish walls arose. Tall minarets and slender towers of many a graceful mosque with low white buildings of the Moorish sway, all rosy-roofed and rich in fairy tracery of dainty arabesques on plaster walls, began to crown those heights where once had stood the grim gray citadels of Spain. Before the Moors, the Christian men of Spain, retreating to the mountain heights, for generations fought to hold their own and once again win back the fair and smiling lands their fathers had called home. And for those years when Spaniard fought with Moor, what sword so ready as My Cid's to fight the Moors and fend off danger from his King? What heart so staunch maintaining loyalty and truth? My Cid, Ruy Diaz, did defeat the Moors in many fair-fought fields. Alone, and of his own brave heart, he gathered to him men that loved him well, and with that loyal band, he won himself a name for bold adventures and high deeds throughout all Christian Spain. Yet for the number of his victories, he earned full many foes, who poisoned King Alphonso's mind and said with hateful lies that he, My Cid, was secretly in league with those dark Moors. In fury then the King did strip My Cid of lands; he ordered him to leave Castile and gave command that none should grant a shelter to My Cid on pain of death or loss of sight.

Ruy Diaz entered Burgos-town. The men and women rush to see him pass, the windows crowd with streaming eyes. On Christian folk a heavy sorrow falls; they shun My Cid nor dare to welcome him. He seeks his home; but finds the portal fast; one little maiden only cries: "O Campeador, we dare not open unto thee for fear lest we should lose our eyes or even life!"

*From the *Poem of the Cid*, the oldest chronicle of Ruy Diaz, written in 1245, about 150 years after his death.

FROM THE TOWER WINDOW

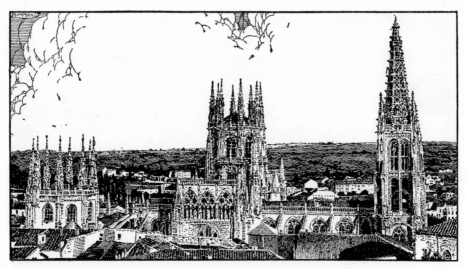

He sighs, My Cid; for very grave his cares. Through Burgos-town he spurs, dismounts him at a Church and offers prayer, then camps upon the river's strand. The least dinero's worth of food he cannot buy; for King Alphonso doth forbid that anyone shall sell to him; yet gather unto him a goodly company, so great the love men bear to him, the Noble-Beard, of Battle famed. And of these all, My Cid loves best bold Alvar-fãnez his good cousin true. Ere cocks begin to crow, My Cid seeks out St. Peter's monastery near the town, where Dame Ximena and his daughters two have taken refuge in these troublous times. My Cid sees Abbot Sancho stand, God's Christian chanting matins for the dawn, and Dame Ximena, too, beseeching aid in prayer.

"Sir Abbot," then Ruy Diaz cries, "I leave my wife and children in your care." Ximena falls upon her knees and weeps, his hands would kiss. Behold they bring his little daughters out, a lady leading each. My Cid clasps fast the little maids. The tears his eyes o'erflow; he deeply sighs: "Ximena, O thou perfect wife of mine. As I do love my soul, so love I thee. Thou seest living we must separate. I shall depart and you remain behind!"

Music for *The Cid*, an opera based on the Spanish epic, was written by the French composer, Jules Massenet (1842-1912).

They part from each as parts the nail from flesh. Now leaves the land My Cid, three hundred lances by his side. Nor houses, lands, nor gold hath he; these must he win by fighting Moors.

Days pass and years; and from the Moors he takes their castles and their towns! What herds of cattle, flocks of sheep, what garments, weapons, gold and steeds! Then ah, how worthily upon his saddle-bow, Ruy Diaz fights and when he cries: "Now strike them, knights, for love of charity!" his warsmen deal such sturdy blows, the Moors must fall or through the fleetness of their steeds escape. He carves him out a province there, My Cid, the Campeador; and so at last he turns his eyes on fair Valencia that owns the Moorish sway. Nine months he lies before the town, forbids their going out or coming in, no trick employs. And when the tenth month comes, they needs must yield. The Campeador rejoices with his men when o'er that soaring Moorish tower, the Alcazar, his Christian banner waves! Now doth his beard increase and longer grow; and thus he speaks: "For love I bear my King, I let no scissors touch my beard since that he exiled me! And may the Moors and Christians talk thereof!"

FROM THE TOWER WINDOW

My Cid is now Valencia's lord. The exiles, how great wealth possess! He gives to each both house and heritage; for thus he proves his love to those who followed him in sorrow as in joy.

Then said My Cid to Alvar-fãnez: "Cousin, an you will; from this my spoil, I'd have you bear my King an hundred steeds and earnestly beseech his leave my wife and daughters to remove from Abbot Sancho's care and hither bring."

Right willingly did Alvar-fãnez then agree; and in that time there came a tonsured one from out the East, Jerome the Bishop called, a man of wisdom deep, in letters learned. The Bishop eager was to see himself engaged afield with Moors; for if in fight he fell a-dealing blows against the infidel, to end of time let Christians weep him not; for so he Paradise would gain! My Cid when that he heard, rejoiced; for in Valencia he wished a bishopric to make, and straightway named as bishop, Don Jerome! All Christendom, how glad that in this Moorish land a Christian bishop now should dwell! Fair tidings those to tell the King!

Good Alvar-fãnez takes his leave. He tells the King the tale of all My Cid hath done, the lands reconquered from the Moors, and placed once more in Christian hands. "My Cid doth deem himself your vassal, hold yourself his lord for all these lands so fairly won," he said. "He begs you take as gift these steeds."

Then to his heart the King was moved for all the loyalty and courage of My Cid; his anger cooled and once again he loved that One-on-hour-propitious-born. Went Alvar-fãnez forth to take Ximena and her daughters to My Cid. With palfreys, mules, and full an hundred men on steeds bedecked with bells and silken coverings, he now equips the dames, that they no poor appearance may present. My Cid was filled with joy which ne'er had higher risen, nor so high. On Babieca, his fleet steed, he rode to meet those three whom he loved best. The mother and the daughters close he drew within his arms; and for their joy they wept. They mount the Alcazar, Valencia's highest tower and see the city far below and on the other hand the sea and all that rich, far-reaching countryside that owned My Cid its lord. Their hands uplift in prayer, they offer thanks to God.

Now when the winter passed, King Yusef of Morocco drew his forces up with fifty times a thousand fully-armed to seek Valencia and fight My Cid. Ximena and her daughters grieved; but good Cid Campeador, he grasped his beard and promised victory! At cock-crow Bishop Don Jerome recited mass. Sprang forth My Cid upon his steed, on Babieca, well with trappings decked. Ah, then behold the bloody sword, the sweating steed! Jerome, most worthy tonsured one, knew not the sum of Moors he slew! And likewise so My Cid. King Yusef fled; and there was booty taken rich beyond belief. As gift, My Cid then sent the King two hundred steeds, and Yusef's royal tent, its tent-poles wrought with gold. What marvels to the courtiers who behold!

"Great grow the riches of My Cid!" Diego and Fernando say, young lords of Carrion. "His daughters let us wed!"

FROM THE TOWER WINDOW

They ask the maidens of the King; and since their rank is high, the King agrees. He bids the Cid to wed his daughters, Dame Elvira and Dame Sol, to these two lords. The maids are still of tender years, but children they. My Cid has little wish to see them wed; yet since the King commands it, he agrees. They plan to meet, those two, for so long parted now, My Cid and Don Alphonso, King. They plan to meet beside the Tagus bank, a mighty stream.

Whoe'er throughout Castile beheld before such handsome mules and palfreys fair of gait, so many goodly pennons on fair shafts, and shields embossed with silver and with gold; pelisses, mantles, cloaks most fair. In colors all are clad both great and small. They meet and he, My Cid, doth cast himself to earth before the King and take the grasses of the field between his teeth, so happy he. But King Alphonso raiseth him and on the mouth saluteth him. He loves him so he cannot tire of him; but gazes on his beard so swiftly grown. Each person present marvels at My Cid and with great feasting now the King doth honor him. Then in his company to fair Valencia journeys back a mighty following to grace the nuptials of the daughters of My Cid.

They think the palace to prepare; from floor aloft with hangings well 'tis decked, such great array of purple, precious stuffs, and lustrous, shining samite as gave joy to see. Full fifteen days they spent upon the weddings fair; then gave My Cid rich gifts, as was his wont, and back the guests returned unto Castile.

Within Valencia about two years the lords of Carrion remained; the love bestowed on them was very great,—white as the sun those fair young maids whom they had wed! Yet were they craven lords, Diego and Fernando both. My Cid one day lay sleeping on a bench when it befell a lion, kept for pleasure in a cage, broke loose and there appeared all suddenly. In great alarm the servitors drew close around My Cid to guard their sleeping lord; but Don Fernando, pale with fear, crept underneath

113

his couch to hide and Don Diego, rushing forth with shrieks, crouched down behind a wine-press and there stained his cloak with the wine. Awoke My Cid, the danger saw. Straight on the lion he advanced and fearless, seized him by the mane. Shame-faced, the lion bowed his head, and let his master lead him to his cage. All marvelled at the deed; but when My Cid asked where his sons-in-law might be, men brought them colorless and pale, Diego stained with wine, before My Cid. Such mirth as filled the court. My Cid, he bade it cease; but those two lords of Carrion were angered in their shame, and hated him, My Cid.

It chanced thereafter in a war with Moors that Don Fernando turned to flee when came a knight and slew Fernando's foe, and let Fernando take the slain Moor's horse, that he might seem the victor in the fight. My Cid, his helmet loose, the coif upon his head in utter-most disorder from the fight, saw his two sons-in-law from battle come and deemed that they had fought like noble knights. He gave to each a sword which he himself had won.

FROM THE TOWER WINDOW

But secretly the vassals of My Cid did smile. These secret sneers the lords could not but see; and though the fault was theirs, they hated more My Cid. Through him they had grown rich; much had he given them and much the booty that had fallen to their lot. They can afford to leave him now and so they plot an evil thing to be avenged on him for all these sneers. They ask permission of My Cid to take their wives and wealth and go back home to Carrion; and though My Cid is grieved to lose his daughters both, he can but give consent. As nail from flesh they part. By night and day, the lords of Carrion do hasten on their march. They cross the mountains clear and so at last they come mid Cor'pes' wood of oak. The trees are high; the branches reach the clouds and wild beasts roam on every hand. A wooded spot and limpid stream they find; and there the lords of Carrion bid fix the tents. Next morn they give the word to load the mighty wealth upon the beasts and all the escort under Felez Muñoz, cousin to the girls, to go ahead along the road. Alone with their two wives they cry: "Now for the matter of the lion, will we take revenge!"

Then from those two young things they take their cloaks and
their pelisses. Save for chemise and ciclaton they leave them nude.
Their sharply pointed spurs they take and saddle girths to beat
their wives. "Nay, kill us rather!" sad, the young things cry.

But those two lords do strike and beat their victims sore; they
scourge them so they all unconscious lie, all blood-bestained the
small chemise and ciclaton. For dead mid Corpes' oaken wood
they leave the two, a prey to savage beasts. Then offering each
to each congratulations for their deed, they journey on.

But Felez Muñoz hath suspected ill. Within a coppice he
is hid; he sees these craven lords pass by without their wives and
hears their talk. He hurries back and what a sight he sees,—
those two fair childish cousins near to death! "My cousins! O
my cousins, for Creator's love awake!" he cries. He brings them
water in his hat. They slowly wake. And still he doth encourage
and exhort until their strength returns, then both sweet forms
within his mantle warm he wraps; he takes them up before him
on his horse; and thus they race the coming night that they perchance may leave the oaken wood ere wild beasts roam.

The news hath reached Valencia the Great. My Cid the
Campeador he grasps his beard. "By this same beard that man
hath never plucked!" he cries. "The lords of Carrion shall suffer
for this deed!"

He sends to King Alphonso asking justice, and full grieved
to hear the sorry tale, the King sends heralds out to bid the Cortes
meet within Toledo, and there render justice to My Cid.

Naught stays the One-on-hour-propitious-born. In goodly
hose and shoes ornate, in tunic rich with gold and cloak of worth,
his beard so long he binds it with a cord, he enters then the royal
hall. Alphonso and his nobles rise. With greatest honor they
receive the man. They bid him sit upon a fair wrought seat. All
gaze upon My Cid within the court. He truly in his trappings
seems a man. For very shame the lords of Carrion dare not

look upon his face. Then spake My Cid before them all and told the shame these lords had wrought. He first demanded that they give him back those swords by him in battle won. The lords of Carrion rejoice that he so little asks and give him back his swords, which on two well-loved knights he then bestows. But now My Cid demands returned the wealth he gave. Hard this for lords of Carrion to hear. Those riches all are spent. If they repay, they must then beg and borrow such a sum. Yet doth the court award this payment to My Cid. Fernando and Diego much lament and cry that those two daughters of My Cid were all unworthy by their birth to be the wives of men so nobly born. They might, they said, aspire to daughters of great emperors and kings. Their sorrows grow; for those two worthy knights on whom My Cid bestowed the swords, do challenge them to fight! Most loath are they! They make excuses many, pale with fear, repenting much the evil deeds they did.

But now the King himself decrees that they must fight. There gather many goodly men and rich this fight to see; it pleaseth all. The lords of Carrion are face to face with those good swords their treachery hath lost. They fear them much, and straight and true the aim of those, My Cid's good knights. Fernando cries: "I vanquished am!" the while Diego shrieks unto the King for aid and flees the lists! How great their shame! How deep disgrace! Who treateth ill sweet woman and deserts, may like befall or e'en a fate more dire! Ruy Diaz grasps his beard. "Be praised the King of Heaven! My daughters are avenged!"

Then came two princes to My Cid, the heirs of Aragon and of Navarre, and asked the hands of fair Elvira and sweet Sol. My Cid hath wed his daughters higher than before. His daughters have become the Queens of Aragon and of Navarre, his relatives today are Kings of Spain; and those two lords of Carrion must bend the knee before the wives they scorned! To Him-on-hour-propitious-born hath come in all things honor; here the story ends.

A CHRONICLE OF KIEV

NOW Vladimir, King of the Russian-land,
  Left the ways of the heathen.
He ordered the idols cast down and some to be cut to pieces.
Perun, the god of thunder, he tied to the tail of a horse,
He bade men to strike him with rods
And drag him down hill to the river.
Unbelievers wept over him and he was cast in the Dnieper.
And there came unto Vladimir people without number.
They waded into the water; they received the holy baptism.
Great was the joy in heaven, but the devil groaned and said:
"Woe is me! I am driven from here!
I shall no longer reign in these lands!"

FROM THE TOWER WINDOW

The Word of Igor's Armament

Retold from an old Russian Epic of the 12th Century

In the days of Oleg, son of woe, feuds were sown in Russia. No longer, as in the time of the good king Vladimir, was the Russian land one in its borders; for Oleg fostered discords and sowed arrows over the land. In those days the warriors rarely walked behind the plough in Russia; they went forth to the battle. Ravens croaked as they divided dead bodies of the fallen and crows chattered flying to the banquet; for Oleg rose up in wrath. He rose up against his uncles; he made common cause with raiders, Turkish Sons of the Devil, the Pagan tribe of Polovtses. Three times he led Russia's foes to harry his native land. Through his offence were many laid low on the green feather-grass of the steppe. And when his eyes closed in death, the Pagans, whom he had led, filled with their bristling sword-blades the lands by the River Don. With envious eyes they looked toward the white-walled city of Kiev, the glittering jewel of all Russia, shimmering in her birchwoods, gorgeous with colored doorways, gleaming with bulb-shaped domes and wonders of metal work. Rich were her monasteries, filled with embroidered vestments, with gold and silver chalices, with jeweled crucifixes. The bodies of the Pagans swayed buoyantly in their saddles as they thought of the plunder ahead.

But the grandson of Oleg, the Grand Prince of Kiev, put discords to sleep for a time. Russian was once again brother unto

The opera *Prince Igor* by the Russian composer, Borodin, has a chorus of Tartar women and oriental dances given in the Khan's camp, while Igor is a prisoner. Cossack dances came to Russia from the Orient.

119

Russian and peace lay in Russian hearts. Once again in the farmyards ducks, geese, swans and pigeons fattened as food for the Great Ones and woodsmen gathered wild honey to make the golden-mead which the Great Ones drank at their feasting. Prince and Boyar again rode forth to the chase and hunted the boar in the forest and Kiev was gay with music, dancing and good cheer.

Then the Grand Prince said on a day: "I will drive out the Sons of the Devil. I will drive the Pagan from Russia!" And he went to the Upper Land to gather more mighty warriors, wishing in the summer to go against the Pagans even to the River Don. But while he was gone from home, his kinsman, the youthful Igor, rash with the fewness of years, thought to seek glory for himself. He thought to drive out the Pagan ere the Grand Prince returned from the north. He said: "I alone will conquer."

Then Igor strengthened his soul by his valor; he sharpened it by the courage of his heart, and having filled himself with a manly spirit, he led his valiant army for the land of Russia into the country of the Pagans. He bade farewell to his wife, the fair young Yaroslavna. He rode from his home on a Tuesday taking with him his boyars, all the following of his druzhina, and together with them likewise, a band of fighting Finns. But as they went toward the river, Igor looked up at the sun; he saw it covered with darkness and covering with darkness his warriors; the bright sun was but as a moon; the day before them was night. And his boyars hung their heads and said: "O Prince, this is not a good omen!"

Still did the strong desire fill the soul of Prince Igor to be to the Russian land a hero above all heroes. Blinded in his blind eagerness to the evil of clear-speaking omens, Igor spake thus to his men:

"O brothers, it is better to be cut to pieces than to bow the head to the heathen. I wish to break the spear in the border of the Pagan land together with you, sons of Russia! O poet of hero's glory, soaring like a nightingale over the tree of thought,

you shall lay your fingers on living strings and sound the glory
of princes. Thus shall you sing for Igor:

> 'The horses neigh
> Beyond the Sula;
> Glory resounds in Kiev;
> Trumpets blare in Novgorod;
> The standards are at Putivl!' "

Then Igor, having thus spoken, forded the river Donets and
came to the river Oskol. There he awaited his brother, his beloved
brother Sevolod, he who was called the Grim Aurochs.

Two days Igor waited. Then came he, the Grim Aurochs, and
he spake to his brother thus: "My only brother, my only light,
glorious Igor, we are both sons of one father! Saddle, O brother,
your swift steeds; for mine are ready for you, having been saddled
in advance. My Kurians are tried warriors nurtured by the
sound of trumpets, rocked in helmets, fed at the point of a spear.
They race over the fields like grey wolves, seeking honour for
themselves and glory for their Prince!"

The two young brothers then went forward on their way.
And there came to them the guards they had sent out to recon-
noitre, and the guards spake thus to the heroes: "We have seen
the army of the enemy and they are riding rapidly."

And Igor cried: "Let us proceed with God's aid." Then he
stepped into the golden stirrup and galloped over the field. Yet

still did the sun bar his way in darkness; night groaned with cries of birds; wolves bristled up and howled a storm in the mountain clefts; eagles screeched and Div, the dark bird of ill-omen, called aloud in the tree-tops! O Russian land, you are lost! You are lost beyond redemption! You are already beyond the mound! Night is long and murky; dawn withholds the light; mists cover the fields; the nightingale's song is silent; the cawing of crows is heard. All through the night the Russians travel; but all through the night, by untrodden ways, the Pagans travel also. The Pagans hasten to the Don. Their carts go creaking at midnight like flocks of swans let loose. O Russian land you are lost!

Early in the morning on the Friday, the Russians saw the army of the Pagan across a little river, old and young drawn up for battle before their encampment of tents. And archers galloped out from the troops of the Polovtses. They sent each an arrow against the Russians and galloped back again ere the Russians had crossed the river. Then Igor and his men pursued them. The Russians struck down their foe. They spread like arrows over the field; they crushed the Pagan host. The Pagans fled from their camp. The Russians gave chase nor halted till they came as far as the tents. But there they stopped for plunder. They seized fair Pagan maidens, gold and gold-worked stuffs. With cloaks of costly velvet, with coats and Pagan lace, they bridged their way across the bogs and muddy places. A red flag, a white pennon, a red plume, a silver cross-beam, these were the trophies he won, Igor, the rash young prince!

Igor and Sevolod dreamed. They dreamed the rash dreams of youth. They thought to win such a battle and yet not stir to the conflict the two great Khans of the Pagans. They thought to make themselves heroes yet not to offend the gerfalcon and the black raven of the heathens. But like grey wolves they come, the two great Khans of the Pagans. They race to the banks of the Don, to the banks of the great River Don.

FROM THE TOWER WINDOW

Very early the next morning a bloody dawn announced the day. Black clouds came from the sea; blue lightnings quivered through them. O Russian land, you are lost! You are lost beyond redemption! You are already beyond the mound!

The earth groans; the rivers flow turbid; dust covers the fields; the banners whisper. The Pagans come from the Don! They come from the sea, and from all sides! Like a forest they appear! They fill the field with their cries! The Russian army recedes. Many are the killed and wounded. Thick lie the Russian shields, crimson upon the field.

Grim Aurochs, brother of Igor! You stand in the van; you pour arrows on the warriors; you thunder with steel swords against their helmets. Wherever you, Aurochs, lead, gleaming with your golden helmet, there fall the heads of the Pagans! How now can you remember the golden throne of your fathers, the caresses of your sweetheart, the peaceful customs of home-days? From early morning until evening, from evening until daylight, fly tempered arrows, thunder the swords against the helmets, resound the steel spears in a strange field. The black earth beneath the hoofs is sown with bones, and watered with blood, and a harvest of sorrow goes up in the Russian land.

What noise is that, what din, so early in the morning? Igor leads his army; he is filled with grief for his brother, his beloved brother Sevolod. The brothers separated on the bank of the swift Kayala. Here the brave Russians ended the feast; they gave their host their fill of bloody wine to drink; they fell for the Russian land. The grass withered from sorrow, and the trees in anguish bent down to the earth. They fought that day until evening and late into the night; and when Sunday began to break, Igor's wild band of Finns were confused and ran away. Igor was then on horseback for his left arm had been wounded; but he followed hard after the Finns to bring them back again. He took his helmet off, that the fleeing might know who he was and rally once more to his side. But none of the Finns, save one, returned to follow their leader. And as Igor rode back toward his troop the Pagans crossed his path, he being alone on the field. Within arrow-shot of his troop, the Pagans made him a prisoner. And while he was held there captive, Igor saw his brother fighting. He saw Sevolod fighting mightily and in his heart he implored that he himself might die rather than see his brother fall dead before his eyes. But Sevolod fought on and on till he had no weapons left.

And Igor cried in sorrow there by the river Kayala: "I now recall my sins before the Lord my God, for I have caused much slaughter and bloodshed in the Christian land, as well as among the Pagans, and I am not worthy to live! Today the punishment of the Lord hath reached me. Where is now my beloved brother? Where are the counselling boyars? Where are the ranks of the soldiers? The Lord has given me fettered into the hands of the Pagans! The Lord has repaid me for my lawlessness and my sins have come down on my head! I see today others receiving the crown of martyrdom, but why can not I, the guilty one, suffer for all of them? O Lord my God, do not reject me! As Thy will, O Lord, is done, so also is Thy mercy unto us, Thy slaves!"

FROM THE TOWER WINDOW

So Igor was unseated from his golden saddle and placed upon the saddle of a slave. His standards fell on the field, his army scattered to the wind. The Pagans overran Russia, demanding as tribute-money a silver coin from each house. Kiev groaned under its sorrow and Chernigov for its misfortunes. Sadness and heavy gloom spread over the Russian land. The city walls were silent; men and women mourned and merriment was dead.

Then the Grand Prince of Kiev saw a troubled dream. He saw himself wrapped in a shroud, lying as one dead, on a sorrowful bed of yew; and all night long he heard the devilish black crows cawing! But when he told of his dreams, his boyars spake to him thus: "Prince, sorrow has poisoned your mind that you dream of such evil omens. It was because of the rashness of those two falcons, your kinsmen, that their wings have been clipped by the Pagans. True, on Kayala River darkness veils the day; Pagans invade the land; fair Pagan maidens sing on the shore of the sapphire sea, tinkling with Russian gold; they sing old times of battle, recall old days of revenge! But we, your druzhina, Prince, are anxious for the battle-feast! We can still bear destruction to these children of the Devil!"

Then did the great Prince of Kiev utter golden words, mingled with his tears: "O, my kinsmen, Igor and Sevolod! Too early did you begin to strike the land of the Pagans with your swords, and ingloriously have you spilled the blood of the Pagans! See what you have done with my silvery hair! You said: "We alone will vanquish! We alone shall gain the glory!' Yet why should not an old man feel young again? Why should not I, like a moulting falcon, drive other birds away, and allow not my nest to be hurt?"

And he sent to the other princes rousing words of need: "Fly from afar, O Russian princes! Come to protect your paternal throne! You have with your discords invited the Pagan hosts against the Russian lands. Put your feet, O lords, into your golden stirrups! Avenge the insult to Russia, the wounds of Igor, the valiant!

"Ricks are stacked with heads; the body is placed on the threshing-floor; the soul is winnowed from the body! Avenge the Russian land, the wounds of Igor, the valiant!"

So spake the Great One of Kiev unto the princes of Russia.

And now is heard the voice of Yaroslavna, the fair young wife of Igor. Yaroslavna's voice is heard; like a cuckoo in a lonely spot she calls plaintively in the morning: "I will fly," she says, "like a cuckoo along the Danube! I will wet my beaver sleeve in the river Kayala! I will wipe off the bloody wounds on the manly body of my prince!"

Yaroslavna weeps in the morning at Putivl town on the wall. "O mighty wind!" she says, "Why do you, on your light wings, carry arrows against my beloved one? Is it not enough for you to blow beneath the clouds, rocking the ships on the sea? Why have you scattered my happiness over the grass of the steppe?"

Yaroslavna weeps in the morning at Putivl town on the wall. "O famous Dnieper," she says, "you have rocked the boats of the Russians. Fondly bring me my sweetheart, that I may not in the morning send my tears after him out to sea."

Yaroslavna weeps in the morning at Putivl town on the wall. "Bright, three times bright sun," she says, "why have you thrust your burning beams on the warriors of my beloved one? Why have you in the waterless plain dried their bows and their quivers in sorrow?"

FROM THE TOWER WINDOW

So Yaroslavna weeps at Putivl town on the wall. But Igor spent that year with the Pagans, and he said: "According to my deserts have I received defeat at Thy hands, O Lord!"

Yet the Pagans, respecting his leadership, did no harm to young Igor. They placed over him fifteen men and five lords' sons to be his guard. They gave him permission to go where he wished and he went a-hunting with the hawk. Moreover, there were with him five or six of his servants and a priest he had brought from Russia that he might know the will of God. And the Lord delivered him out of the hand of the Pagans for the many prayers of the Christians and the many tears which they shed for him. For one among the Pagans, a man by the name of Lavor, had a blessed thought. "I will take you to Russia!" he said. But Igor made answer, "For glory's sake I did not in the hour of danger run away from my druzhina, and even now will I not, by fleeing, walk the inglorious road."

Then Igor's advisers said: "You harbour a proud thought, O Igor, and one not pleasing to God. Why do you not consider that the Pagans, returning from war, will of a certainty slay you! Get you up and seek freedom. Return in haste to your homeland! Come again with your prince against this Pagan host; you will yet by your prince's side make the heathen drink the cup of defeat and sorrow!"

So Prince Igor took their advice. Finding an opportune time, he sent his attendant to Lavor. "Cross you with a led horse to the other side of the Tor and await me there!" he said.

The sea is agitated at midnight; mists are borne in the darkness. God shows to Igor a way out of the land of the Pagans into the country of Russia, to his prince's golden throne.

The evening twilight has gone out. Igor sleeps; Igor is awake. His steed is ready at midnight. Lavor whistles beyond the river! All is ready for flight! Now no more will Prince Igor be found in the tents of the Pagans!

Igor arose; he bowed before the image of the Lord and the honourable cross, and he said: "Lord, knower of hearts! If Thou, Master, wilt save me, unworthy one,"—and he took the cross and the image; he lifted the side of the tent and stealthily crawled out from under. Gambling and feasting, his guards, drunken with drinking of kymys, thought that the Prince was asleep. He waded across the river. He mounted the steed held by Lavor. He rode away in the darkness. The earth resounded, the grass rustled, the Pagans' tents trembled. But Igor raced like an ermine in the reeds, like a white duck over the water. As a falcon he flew through the mist, and where he flew as a falcon, Lavor raced as a wolf. They killed geese and swans for breakfast, they killed geese and swans for dinner; they killed geese and swans for supper.

Thus they came to the plains that lie by the river Donets; they crossed the river in safety and Igor spake thus to the river: "O Donets, great is your honour! You have rocked the Prince on your wave! You have spread out for him green grass on your silver banks! You have cloaked him with your warm mists! You have guarded him as a duck, as a gull on the waves of your waters!"

FROM THE TOWER WINDOW

It is not magpies that are a-flutter. It is they, the sons of the Devil, the mighty Khans of the Pagans riding on Igor's track. Silent, they urge their swift steeds towards the river Donets. But they do not overtake Igor. To them he is lost forever.

Hard it is for you, O head, to be without your shoulders; ill it is for you, O body, to be without a head. Even so is the Russian land without Igor. Igor returns to Russia. The sun shines in the heaven,—Prince Igor in the land of Russia! Maidens sing at the Danube; their voices are carried lightly over the sea to Kiev. Igor crosses the mountain to the church of the Holy Virgin. He comes again to his wife, to Yaroslavna, the fair. No more does she weep in the morning at Putivl town by the wall. She has him again, her beloved, to hold in a fond embrace. He comes again to Kiev, to his kinsman, the Grand Prince of Kiev! All the country is happy, all the towns rejoice! They sing songs to the elder princes, and then to Prince Igor and Sevolod. Hail, Princes and Druzhina, who battle for the Christians against the Pagan host! Glory to the Princes! Glory! Glory! Amen!

Frithjof, the Viking

Retold from the Norse Saga of Frithjof

IN THE royal halls King Be'le reigned. Power and might were his, and descent from a noble line of kings, yet his best beloved friend, his old brother-in-arms, closest of all to his heart, was none other than Thor'sten the Viking, born of no royal blood, but son of an humble yeoman. Staunch were the hearts of these two in devotion to one another. As the fast-passing winters silvered their heads, their friendship only grew deeper and stronger. Throughout all the Northern lands, in hall and bower, the skalds sang songs of that beautiful friendship.

Now King Bele had two sons and one lovely daughter, Ing'-e-borg the Fair. But Thorsten had one only son, the stalwart stripling Frith'jof. When Ingeborg and Frithjof were little more than smiling babes, their fathers committed them to the care of a third trusty friend, old Hil'ding, who dwelt at a distance from the court in a rich and handsome farm-house that rose from the midst of well-kept barns and blossoming fields and pastures. There in sturdy simplicity Ingeborg and Frithjof passed together a pure and joyous childhood,—she a soft-budding, sweet-blushing rose, and he an oak, straight and lordly. How happy was he when, as a mere boy, he took her first in his swift-skimming skiff out on the blue waters of the fjord, and she clapped her hands in childish glee as he set the snowy sail; how happy when he first lifted her up to peer at the eggs and little ones in the nests of the beautiful song-birds that lay hidden amongst the trees. No brook was ever so wide that he did not carry Ingeborg across, her little arms tight about his neck, her head against his breast. The first blossom in the woodland peeping up beneath snow, the first luscious ripened strawberry red in its tangle of leaves, the first golden ear of corn,—he carried them all to his little queen.

But ah! almost before old Hilding knew it, it was no more

these childish treasures, but a great bear, slain without a weapon in breast to breast struggle, that the young hero bore slung across his shoulder to lay at Ingeborg's feet. When winter came and the long home evenings, with all the housemates gathered together before the blazing hearth, young Frithjof read aloud the ancient lays of Odin, the All-father, and Valhalla's heavenly halls, but not one of all the goddesses, not even Freya the Fair, seemed to Frithjof more lovely than his own sweet playmate sitting there in the ruddy glow of the flaming logs, her hair in golden ringlets, her brow as white as the new-driven snow, her blue eyes soft and gentle as the tender sky in spring.

And Ingeborg herself, as she sat at her loom through the day, singing the deeds of heroes, and weaving into her tapestry with wool of many colors the figures of knights and soldiers and the heroes of her singing, began to make her hero more like in face and bearing to the stately Frithjof. Above all others on earth Ingeborg and Frithjof loved each other.

Then the heart of old Hilding misgave him.

"Beware my son," he said to his ward. "Let not this love of thine master thee. No good can come of it. Remember, Ingeborg is daughter of a King and thou art but son to a yeoman."

But Frithjof laughed the warning to scorn.

"The free-born man is second to none," he cried. "The world is the freeman's. I will do such deeds that the King himself will be proud to give me his daughter."

Now came the day when old Bele and Thorsten sitting side by side in the palace with faces lined and marked till they looked like ancient rocks deeply graven with runes, spake thus to one another: "Our day is done. For earthly sights our eyes grow dim. Ever nearer shines Valhalla. Ere the white-armed Valkyrs with flying hair bear us off to those heavenly halls, let us call our sons before us and give them good counsel. They should be ever knit firmly together as we have been in closest unity and love."

So came the sons—first Bele's eldest, dark and gloomy with stern and sullen brow, Hel'ge, heir to the throne, then Half'dan, Bele's younger lad, with sunny locks and noble features, yet too soft,—a maid almost, in warrior's guise. Last of all came Frithjof, by a head the tallest of the three, standing between the King's two sons like the full and radiant noon between shy dawn and lowering dusk.

"Sons," spake the King, "my day is sinking low and yours will soon be breaking. As you are brothers, so be friends and rule the land in harmony. Let Power stand guard at your borders, that no enemy enter in, but let Peace hold gentle sway within the land in your safe keeping. Your swords should never threaten, but protect. Guard well your people and act ever in unity with them, for a king is naught without the people. Be never hard when thou art King, O Helge,—only firm. Remember, gentleness alone leads a noble heart to right-doing, even as the Spring's mild breath opens the earth which wintry frosts but harden. And thou, Halfdan, be mindful that cheerfulness graces a wise man, yet do carelessness and frivolity ill beseem a King."

When the King had made an end of speaking Thorsten thus addressed his son:

"Honor the gods, O Frithjof, for reverence becomes a man. Obey the King and never envy him whose place is above thine own. Thou hast great bodily strength, but remember, such a gift is worthless unless joined with wisdom to direct it right. Turn thee from evil; bend thy will to what is good and noble, and do right. Thus wilt thou not have lived in vain."

Many more were the loving words spoken by the old warriors on that day. They told the youths of their long friendship and how through joy and sorrow, they had ever stood together, hand in hand, sharing alike the changeful gifts of life. And both bequeathed their friendship to their sons as a jewel of greatest price. Last of all, King Bele committed his beloved daughter,

FROM THE TOWER WINDOW

Ingeborg, with many tender words, to the care of his two sons.

"When we are gone," he said, "old friend Thorsten and I, lay our bodies in two mounds, which you shall raise, one on each side of the blue bay. Its waves shall sing our dirge, but when the pale moon pours on the mountains her silver sheen, and the midnight dew lies cool upon the fields, then we two will still commune together in closest comradeship. And now, sons, fare ye well. Go back to your work and play. For us, our way lies to All-father's halls,—the place of rest, for which we long as long the weary rivers for the sea. Go, and the grace of Frey and Thor and Odin go with you."

Not many months thereafter, Bele and Thorsten had departed from this life for the glories of Valhalla, and their bodies, as directed, lay side by side in mounds on each side of the bay. Then went a herald riding through the land from farm to farm, from home to home, summoning all the people to the Ting, the general meeting of true-hearted free-men, in whose breasts is safely housed the honor of the nation. There Helge and Halfdan were elected joint-kings to rule the realm together.

Frithjof, too, entered now into his inheritance—the homestead of his father at Framnäs, with hills and valleys and woods, three miles each way, and the sea as boundary on one side. The heights were crowned with birchwood, and many a shining lake mirrored mountains and forests where antlered elks stalked majestic. In the gently sloping fields the golden barley ripened in the sun, and rye so tall that a man might hide in it. The green and blooming pastures in the valleys were dotted with herds of kine and flocks of sheep as white and fleecy as the cloudlets in the sky. In the stables there stood in stately rows four and twenty fiery steeds, their manes braided with red ribbons, their hoofs glistening with polished shoes. But the wonder of the place was the banquet-hall, a palace in itself, built solidly of fir-trunks. So large it was, that six hundred guests hardly filled it at the Yule-tide feast. The table of oak stretched the whole length of the hall, and was waxed to a polish as bright as steel. The raised platform at the host's end was adorned with two statues of gods, Odin with royal mien, and Frey with the sun on his brow. Between the two was the host's seat, covered with a huge black bearskin, with scarlet mouth and silver-mounted claws. It seemed but yesterday that Thorsten himself sat there, gravely and yet genially entertaining his friends while the logs blazed high on the deep stone hearth in the middle of the hall, stars peered down through the smoke-escape in the roof, and the firelight gleamed and glinted from the armor that hung on the walls.

But of all the family treasures which now fell to Frithjof, the most dearly prized were the ancient and peerless sword, Ang'ur-wa'del, and the great dragon-ship, El-lide'. Long stretched as a sea serpent rose the prow of Ellide, the neck swung aloft in graceful curves, the head with red mouth wide open. Her sides were blue, with spots of gold; at the stern her mighty tail uncoiled in rings, silver scaled; her sails were black tipped with scarlet, and when she unfurled them she could fly like the storm-wind, and far exceed in fleetness the eagle's flight. When filled with men in armor she seemed like a floating castle. Great was the fame of that ship. Far and wide was she known as peerless in the North. Over all these treasures now was Frithjof master, and he sat at the funeral feast a tearful host on his father's seat which should henceforth be his own.

When the earth had donned once more her robe of green, few dragon-ships still lingered in the harbors. Most of that bold craft had sallied forth on foreign ventures as was the Norseman's wont. But Frithjof's thoughts did not roam the seas these moon-lit nights of lovely May. He sought the solitude of the woods. While Ellide swung restlessly in the harbor tugging at her anchor, his thoughts were full of Ingeborg alone. And so one day he loosed the ship. She bounded from her moorings, and bore him with swelling sails across the bay to the spot where Helge and Halfdan sat, on King Bele's grave-mound, holding open court of justice. Proudly, yet respectfully, Frithjof spoke.

"O Kings, I love fair Ingeborg as mine own soul, and crave her at your hands to be my bride. Such, surely, was your father's wish, for it was by his will we two grew up together. True, my father was neither king nor earl, yet he did such deeds as give his name high place in all the songs of skalds. I, myself, could easily win a kingdom, yet would I liefer stay at home and guard your realm for you, protecting with my sword your royal castle and the poor man's hut alike. We are here on your father's mound. Hear ye, his sons, and do as he would have wished."

But King Helge started to his feet and spake in scornful tones.

"Our sister is not for the bonder's[1] son. Though thou shouldst by force of arms compel men to hail thee greatest of all Norseland's sons, never should maid of Odin's blood mate with a lowborn adventurer! Nor is there any call for thee to take thought for my realm. I can hold it and care for it myself. If thou wouldst be my servant, there is a place for thee amongst my men-at-arms!"

At words so hateful, the warm-welling spring of friendship in Frithjof's heart closed tight. Fierce burning wrath sprang up instead. In clarion tones he cried, "Thy servant I will never be, black-hearted King. Take heed that thou keep well thy boast and find no need for my good sword. It is a trusty blade." And he clove with one furious stroke King Helge's golden shield that hung on the limb of a tree above him. As it fell with an ominous clang to the ground, Frithjof strode from the place, black-browed with that anger that consumes like fire and withers in the human heart all gently springing buds of great and good desires.

Meantime, in a nearby kingdom dwelt the old King Ring, a man of such piety and wisdom as were famed throughout the Northland. The verdant valleys and shady woods of his happy realm never resounded with the evil noise of war. Peacefully the

[1] yeoman's

crops ripened there and roses bloomed, for Justice sat enthroned, severe yet gracious, on the judgment seat, and Freedom dwelt with Peace in happy harmony. At the meetings of the Ting, every man was free to speak his mind without restraint or fear, and like a father was the King beloved by all his subjects.

But now King Ring's good wife was dead, and though he loved her with undying love, he saw necessity, for the sake of his country and his motherless babes, to choose himself another bride.

"My old time friend, King Bele, left a daughter," he said. "For her hand will I sue. True, she is but young, just budding into bloom, playmate of lilies and roses, while many a winter's snow lies on my scanty locks. Still, should she find in her heart some love to give an honest man, though he be old, and womanly care for tender motherless babes, then fain would my winter share with her spring this throne."

So he sent warriors and skalds with attendants many to bear gifts and honorable offers to King Bele's sons. Right royally was the train received, but when King Helge with his priests consulted at the altar to inquire the will of the gods concerning this marriage, the omens were so dark, portending such disaster, that Helge, ever a slave to dark and gloomy superstitions, rejected King Ring's wooing right curtly, while childish Halfdan with scant respect made an open joke at the old man's expense.

Bitterly angered, the envoys departed. All the story of their insulting dismissal they told to King Ring. The good old man, who would have accepted graciously a courteous refusal, answered little, but his words were grim. With his spear he struck the iron shield on the bough of an ancient linden tree, the signal that summoned all the people to arms. War heralds hurried right and left. Soon, in answer, the dragon-ships came crowding, with their blood-red crests, and helmets nodded in the breeze.

King Helge heard of this warlike array and was greatly perturbed in spirit, for though great pride of heart was his, he was utterly lacking in courage. Moreover, he knew that King Ring, although he loved not war, was all the more a powerful foe for the very reason that he never gave battle without just cause.

Knowing that King Ring's first attempt would doubtless be to carry Ingeborg away, Helge ordered his sister to retire into the enclosure of Balder's temple, thus placing her in the pure and gentle keeping of the best beloved among the gods. The temple of Balder was to all the peoples of the North the most sacred of all sanctuaries, and whatever woman or maid had taken refuge there was secure from the approach of any man. Death awaited him who should force a way into that holy place. There lovely Ingeborg sat day after day, sad and tearful, bending over her embroidery frame, plying her needle or sorting her silks and golden threads.

Frithjof, meantime, lived on, moody and moping in the seclusion of his freehold at Framnäs. He nursed his wrath and would not go to Helge's aid. All his thoughts centered instead on one fierce intent,—he would see Ingeborg once more, the sunshine of his life. No matter what the cost, he would enter the sacred enclosure of Balder. He sent secret word to Ingeborg that he was coming, and his good ship Ellide bore him by night to the unguarded shore of the temple grounds. There Ingeborg was waiting in the pale dusk of a northern night in spring. How joyous was their greeting, though likewise full of tears. True, Ingeborg was frightened at Frithjof's breaking thus into the sanctuary of

137

Balder, but he led her reverently to the carven statue of the gentle god and said: "Balder, the good, can never be angry at the innocent meeting of two lovers. We mean no disrespect to him. Before his altar we will ever bend the knee."

Thus many a happy meeting they two had in secret after that first daring step. But at length, with many prayers and tears and a thousand coaxing ways, Ingeborg won Frithjof's promise, when next the Ting should meet presided over by her brothers, to go before the people, once more ask her of the kings, and offer them his hand in friendship.

So came the day when free-men gathered to the Ting. On Bele's mound from top to bottom Norseland's free-men stood in ordered ranks, with hand on hilt, and shield to shield. On the stone judgment seat King Helge sat, dark as a thunder cloud, and by him Halfdan, a grown up boy, leaned carelessly on his sword. Suddenly Frithjof stood before them.

"King Helge," he said, "War stands at the borders. Thy realm is threatened. Give me thy sister and my arm is thine to fight thy battles loyally. Cast prejudice aside. Let all ill-feeling be forgotten. Here is my hand."

A murmur as of rising sea-waves swept over the Ting. A thousand swords struck applause against a thousand shields, and voices here and there swelled into one mighty roar. "O give him Ingeborg. His is the best sword in all the land."

In vain. With cold contempt King Helge said:

"The bonder's son might even yet call Ingeborg bride. But never he who sacrilegiously broke into Balder's temple. Speak, Frithjof. Didst thou not commit that crime? Say—yes or no?"

A shout went up from the ring of men. "Say no, O Frithjof! We will believe thy word and woo for thee. Thorsten's son is the equal of Kings. Say no! and Ingeborg is thine."

But Frithjof answered: "The weal or woe of all my life hangs on my answer, yet would I never tell a lie to buy Valhalla's joys, much less the joys of earth. I did in truth enter the sacred precincts of Balder's temple to speak with Ingeborg, but did not thereby disturb the peace of that holy place."

A groan of horror ran throughout the Ting. Those nearest Frithjof recoiled with blanching cheeks, as though his deed had been a crime unspeakable. In tones low and ominous Helge said:

"Our laws leave me free to order either death or exile for such a deed as thine. Yet will I be merciful. Far out on the western sea there lies a cluster of islands over which Earl An'gan-tyr rules. As long as Bele lived the earl sent yearly tribute, but not since Bele's death. Go! demand the tribute and bring it home. Thus and thus only mayest thou redeem thy life and honor."

Bitterly Frithjof sought once more Ingeborg in the temple. At first in his madness he urged her to flee with him, flee far away to the smiling blue seas of distant Greece, to that land of soft and balmy breezes, so different from the cold and hardy Northland. But Ingeborg, though all her heart was longing, would not listen to his pleading. She would not flee away in lawlessness and let Frithjof taint his honor further still. By her gentle pleading she persuaded him to go and expiate his guilt by seeking Angantyr.

"Then," he cried, "when my task is performed, my honor cleared, and I am free from guilt, I will return and demand thee of the open Ting. That and not Helge is thy rightful guardian."

And he gave to Ingeborg, as pledge of his undying love, a wondrous golden armlet curiously wrought and adorned with a matchless ruby. So he went, and Ingeborg, from the mighty rocks on the shore, watched the dragon-ship Ellide make off to the distant sea. Long and wistfully she watched, her heart sad and full of forebodings.

Hard was Frithjof's journey westward and through terrific tempests, but at last, storm-battered and weary, he and his men arrived at the court of Earl Angantyr, Lord of the Orkneys.

Splendid indeed was the hall of the Earl, and far less crude than the halls of the Northland. Frithjof's walls had nought to cover the bare rough-hewn planks, but the Earl's were hung with gilt leather hangings stamped with many a cunning design. Instead of a hearth in the middle of the floor, Earl Angantyr's hall had marble mantles at both ends of the room with chimneys so well constructed that no smoke remained inside, and no soot blackened the walls. The windows had panes of glass, and for lighting at night there were silver sconces with waxen candles instead of the smoky but fragrant pine chip stuck in a chink of the planking to which Frithjof was accustomed. High on a dais in a chair of massive silver the Earl sat in state, his golden helmet and corselet flashing. He wore a rich purple mantle embroidered with stars and bordered with bands of ermine. Courteously he received Frithjof, for Thorsten had been his good friend.

When Frithjof had eaten and drunk, he frankly told Earl Angantyr that he had come for tribute. As he spoke thus boldly, a silence fell upon all in the hall, but at length Earl Angantyr said:

"Tribute I never paid. I held Bele in honor but never was vassal of his. As to his heirs, I know nothing of them. If they have any claim, let them be men and come and enforce it themselves. But Thorsten was my friend and this is my gift to my old friend's son—" So speaking he gave to Frithjof a belt-pouch worked in green with a clasp of rubies and a tassel of spun gold. The pouch was filled full of golden coins. "Do with this gift as pleases thee. If it be thy wish, give it over unto King Helge when thou returnest, but do thou and thy men stay with us the winter through, I pray thee."

So Frithjof remained in the Orkneys through the winter, but at the first breath of spring in the air, at the first touch of green in the thawing fields, he thanked his host and once again entrusted himself to the sea. Merrily Ellide drew the silver furrow over the dark blue plain.

What joy it is to the mariner to set the sails for home, to

FROM THE TOWER WINDOW

watch for the smoke which rises from his own hearth, for the rock from which a faithful maid has daily looked for him out to sea. So watched Frithjof with beating heart and dimming eyes as he neared the rocky northern shore. This is his own land and those are his own woods. There is the temple of Balder where his beloved Ingeborg awaits him. And now he can hear the waterfall which rushes headlong down the rocks. He rounds the headland. A moment more and he will see the roof of his homestead above the trees. He looks and rubs his eyes and looks again. There is no sign of his beloved Framnäs anywhere. Yet stay! A tall chimney stack, bare and black, rises from the midst of a heap of ruins. He looks and looks again. His heart stands still. Then he leaps ashore. Everywhere is a waste of cinders, ashes, charred and broken stones. Nowhere is there a sign of life. Only his faithful hound springs to him in wild glee and his favorite courser, milk-white with golden mane, comes bounding from the woods. A moment more and old Hilding stood suddenly by the side of the broken-hearted man.

"Alas, dear son!" he cried. "There was a battle with King Ring, just one, soon after thou didst go. Despite his boyishness, King Halfdan showed himself a man, but Helge lost heart and fled, and that was the end. As he passed thy homestead in flight he burned it to the ground. Then the brothers had no choice. King Ring would accept of no peace offering but their sister. Poor Ingeborg! How that brave and gentle spirit sorrowed! In these arms of mine, I lifted her from the saddle on her wedding day, slender and swaying as a lily stalk. King Helge caught sight of thy bracelet on her arm. Roughly he tore it off with a curse. Now by her wish thy last beloved gift is on Balder's arm, in his sacred keeping, but Ingeborg is the bride of King Ring."

Violently then Frithjof burst forth with words of madness in his mighty grief. "The coward! To rob the eagle's nest when the eagle was flown! I will repay him!"

141

It was Midsummer Night. Over the hills stood the midnight sun, blood-red and beamless. It was not day, it was not night— a something grey and weird between. On that night was held a yearly festival of sacrifice to Balder, and Frithjof knew full well that the priestly Helge would be found in Balder's Temple. Wild with grief and fury he rushed to the spot where Helge stood by the altar stone. At sight of him the blood left Helge's face. Frithjof spoke in a voice like the storm wind for fury.

"Here is thy tribute. Take it. Then here by Balder's pyre we fight for life or death."

As he spoke he took from his belt Earl Angantyr's heavy purse and hurled it straight at Helge's head. Blood spurted from the royal mouth and nose, Helge's knees gave way and senseless he sank to the ground.

"What!" mocked Frithjof. "Canst thou not stand the touch of thine own gold, thou most dastardly of Norseland's sons?"

Then he turned, scarce knowing what he said, to the statue of Balder. "And thou, pale Balder, check thine anger, for by thy leave, I must have that bracelet upon thine arm. It was never meant for thee."

He snatched at the bracelet to strip it off in his fury, but it seemed grown fast to the statue's arm. At last with a mighty wrench he jerked it free, but the statue swayed as he did so and fell headlong into the altar fire while the priests stood speechless with horror. In a twinkling the flames leapt upward and caught at the beams of the roof. At that awful sight, Frithjof awakened suddenly to the sacrilege of his deed. For a moment he stood transfixed. Then rushing to the doors he cried, "Open wide the doors. Get out the people. The temple burns. Water! Pour water! Pour the sea!"

From all directions men came running. A chain was quickly formed from the temple to the beach. Buckets ran from hand to hand and soon the water was hissing, sputtering on the heated

FROM THE TOWER WINDOW

wood. Frithjof climbed with frenzied bravery to the top of the threatened roof, and sitting there astride, midst the hideous flames and smoke, he flooded all with water as the buckets were passed up to him. His voice never ceased ringing out commands. He alone directed the work. But all was in vain. The flames he had started raged with the same relentless fury as those but now raging within his own breast. It was as though gentle Balder, roused to wrath, had meant to show him to the full the fierce destructive nature of that consuming fire he had nourished but now within his own heart. From the temple the flames spread to the trees of the surrounding grove, licking the curling shrivelling foliage up, sweeping with a roar like the tempest, challenging the very heavens. At last, from a sea of fire, the grove suddenly collapsed into a wilderness of glowing stumps, a vast heap of dead grey ashes and embers like angry red eyes. Early morning showed the night's awful work of destruction. Silently the people dispersed, and Frithjof went his way alone, filled full of the horror of his deed, made an outcast from among men by the frenzy of his fury, weeping the scalding tears of a strong man's despair.

For Frithjof now there seemed nothing to do but go to sea in his dragon-ship and lead the life of a Viking. Three years long he roamed the seas in his floating castle, the sore and restless spirit within driving him to many a wild adventure, till his name was named throughout the North for the crude bold courage of conquest. But in all this was nought to bring real content to the sorrowing soul of Frithjof. When he reached those softly smiling seas of sunny Greece, that once he had described to Ingeborg as a place of such delight, he was overcome with homesick longing for the rough and rugged Northland and for Ingeborg. And so he turned his dragon-ship at last to the realm of King Ring, with one thought only in his heart. He must see Ingeborg. He must.

It was Yule-tide. King Ring, serene and gracious, sat at the head of his own festive board with his queen fair and gentle beside him,—spring and autumn strangely mated. Suddenly a stranger stood in the doorway, an old man of enormous stature, wrapped in a bear skin, and leaning on a staff. At sight of him a company of youthful retainers by the door laughed and exchanged jeering glances. The stranger's eyes shot forth blue lightnings. With one hand he seized the nearest of the scoffers, a flippant beardless youth, and with no effort whatosever stood him on his head. At that the others grew silent and King Ring called the man to him.

"What is thy name and whence camest thou?" he said.

"My name is nothing to thee," said the stranger. "Misery is my country, Want my patrimony. Yesternight I slept with a wolf. Tonight I come to thee!"

When the King had heard all this he said quietly:

"Come, sit thee down by me, but drop that clumsy disguise. I know thou art no old man and I like not deceit."

So the guest let the shaggy pelt fall back from his head, and there in the old man's place stood one in all the splendor of youth. From his brow long golden locks fell to his shoulders.

FROM THE TOWER WINDOW

A blue velvet mantle thrown back from his breast showed a broad silver belt on which was graven a hunt with flying hart and pursuing hounds. Broad bands of gold glittered on his arms. By his side hung his sword. Thus the hero stood revealed! Into the Queen's pale cheeks the blood shot quickly, even as a snow field flushes with reflection of the crimson Northern Lights.

"Thou art welcome," said the King, "to our Yule-tide feast."

Amid a profound and reverent silence the boar was brought in, the emblem of Frey, the sun god, who from this, the longest night of the year, begins to gather strength to overcome the evil brood of winter giants. The boar was a mighty forest beast, skilfully roasted whole with wreaths of evergreens around his neck and shoulders, and an apple in his mouth. As the bearer set the heavy burden down upon the table, the King and all his guests bent the knee. Then the feasting began.

"Come now, my Queen," cried King Ring. "Serve our guest with mead."

Quietly Ingeborg took a horn mounted with hoops of gold that stood on bright silver feet upon the table before her, and filled it to the brim. Then she offered it with downcast eyes to Frithjof. Thereafter the skald took the harp and began to sing. High ran the harmless merriment. And ere the evening was done King Ring had invited his guest to stay with him all winter.

Frithjof made no promise, yet from day to day he lingered. Ingeborg gave no sign that she knew him, not even a glance, and a stern feeling of honor kept Frithjof from speaking save as an utter stranger to the Queen. Well he knew that King Ring regarded as his enemy that Frithjof whom he had never seen, but who once had wooed his wife. Yet now the old man seemed more and more to take delight in his unknown guest's companionship; he would hear of no excursion, no amusement without him. On a certain day the King and Queen and all their court went on a sleighing and skating expedition across the frozen waters of the fjord. King

Ring himself drove a famous Swedish trotter hitched to a swan-shaped sleigh, with Ingeborg in her nest of furs by his side. Frithjof on skates was racing the trotter to the court's amazement and delight. Suddenly there was a shriek of horror. Sleigh and horse had broken through a thin spot on the ice and almost disappeared. A moment more and they would be sucked by the current under the ice. But in that instant, Frithjof was on the spot. He grasped the horse's head at the bit, and with one pull had him out on his feet. Then he helped him drag the sleigh with its precious human load beyond the line of danger.

"A good pull and a strong!" cried the King in admiration. "That wonder of strong men, mine enemy, Frithjof, could not have done better!" And now he pressed Frithjof so earnestly to remain until spring that at last the young man gave his promise.

In due time spring came with chirping of birds and woodland foliage and long, long days. Once more the rivers ran blithely singing, glad of their liberty, to the sea. A great hunt had long been planned to open the season. Bows creaked, arrows rattled, steeds pawed the ground, and at last she appeared for whom all were waiting—Ingeborg, the Lady of the Hunt, alas! so beautiful

FROM THE TOWER WINDOW

that Frithjof must needs turn his eyes away. All was ready. Off they went. Horns blowing, falcons soaring, garments flying! Over hill and dale, heigho!

King Ring could not ride so fast as the others and he and Frithjof were thus left far behind, for Frithjof stayed ever courteously by the old man's side. Wearied out, the King at last dismounted from his horse to rest in a quiet grove midst ancient elms and birches. Frithjof took off his mantle and spread it on the ground. There King Ring stretched his weary limbs and soon fell asleep.

As he slumbered, hark! a blackbird sang into Frithjof's ear:

"Haste, Frithjof, strike the old man while he slumbers and none are by to see. Then take the Queen, for rightfully she is thine!"

Frithjof listened, but hark! in the other ear a white bird sang.

"If no human eye can see, still All-father's eye is upon thee. Villain, the man is old and unarmed. Thou canst not kill him."

Thus by turns the two birds sang, till Frithjof drew his sword in horror, and to thrust temptation from him, flung the blade far off with violence. Then the blackbird flew away but the white bird soared on light pinions high up into the sunlight and its joyful carol was like the tone of a silver bell.

Abruptly the old King rose from his slumber.

"Where is thy sword?" he cried.

"It was not safe in my hand. I flung it far from me," Frithjof replied.

"Hear then, O youth," said King Ring. "I did not sleep as thou didst suppose but now. I only wished to test thee. Thou art Frithjof. I have known thee from the moment thou didst enter my hall, but well have I seen in these last moments that thou art a man to be trusted. I pity thee and forgive thine attempt to deceive me. I am an old man and soon will be rejoicing in Valhalla. When I am gone, take thou my Queen—she is thine by right, and guard my realm for my infant son. But until I go,

147

abide with me and be my son. There is no longer a feud between us."

Deeply Frithjof marveled at the old King's greatness of soul,
humbly he acknowledged it, yet still in his heart burned the
memory that he was an outcast from men by reason of his sin in
Balder's temple, and for such as he there could be little hope of
good. So he gloomily made up his mind to take his leave of the
lovely Ingeborg.

On a certain day he came to say farewell, but in that very
hour, King Ring departed this life to come into All-father's presence. What, then, could Frithjof do but linger?

In an open field under the blue canopy of heaven met the Ting.
A new king must be chosen. There stood Frithjof straight and
tall upon the judgment stone, and close to him the little gold-
haired child of Ingeborg, King Ring's sole son. A murmur passed
around the circle of men as they looked on Frithjof's stalwart form
and coveted him for a leader.

"The child is too young to rule us," they said.

But Frithjof raised the little one upon his shield.

"Behold your King!" he cried, "the country's blooming hope!
See how at ease he stands upon the unsteady shield. My sword
shall guard his kingdom, and on his brow some day my hand shall
place his father's crown."

Standing on the shield, the child looked up with eyes as bold
as an eagle's, and when he had tired of this novel game, he sprang
with a royal fearlessness from that great height to the ground.
With a roar of delight the Ting greeted this daring feat and men
cried out: "We choose thee King. Be as thy father great and good.
And let Earl Frithjof rule in thy place until thou growest a man.
Do thou, Earl Frithjof, take the mother of the boy to be thy wife!"

But Frithjof paid no heed. He only kissed the little King upon
his brow in homage, and strode forth alone and silent, his grief
for his mighty sin still keeping him from Ingeborg. Led by his

148

FROM THE TOWER WINDOW

deep repentance, he wandered back to that blackened grove and temple of his crime, longing, longing for forgiveness.

"Cannot repentance and a blameless life atone for a moment's madness?" he cried, and threw himself in mighty grief and sorrow on his father's mound, praying to know how he might redeem himself. As he lay there he slept and in his sleep saw a vision. A wonderful new temple he saw, a temple of marvellous beauty in place of the mass of ruins he had made, its dome of crystal pure and blue as virgin ice or the winter sky. Frithjof gazed in awe upon that structure, and then awaking, cried with joy, "The sign! I am to rebuild Balder's temple fairer than ever before. O joy that it is given me to atone!"

And so Frithjof set himself to work to redeem his sin of destructive fury by building anew the temple. More beautiful than ever, with a dignity more stately, a substance more enduring, it rose again, and when the work was done, the day of consecration came. Two by two twelve maidens entered the sacred place, robed richly in cloth of silver, the bloom of roses in their cheeks and in their innocent hearts. In graceful stately dance they moved around the altar as woodland fairies dance on the grassy mounds while morning dew yet sparkles on the grass. And as they danced they sang the sacred lay of Balder.

Frithjof stood leaning on his sword spellbound. It was as though his days of Viking life with all their lawlessness were passing from him altogether, while the joys and dreams of his boyhood came trooping around him, blue-eyed, flower-crowned, smiling, beckoning. Higher and higher his soul was lifted above the lowly haunts of human hatred, human vengeance. One by one the iron bands of dark enslaving human passions that had held his breast oppressed, fell off as winter's ice melts from some mighty rock. The sunshine of peace and love flooded his heart. He could have held the world in fond encircling arms.

Now entered Balder's high priest, tall and of commanding

presence, with silver beard flowing down to his girdle, and heaven's own graciousness in his mild and noble countenance. Frithjof's heart was thrilled with reverent awe as the old man spoke.

"Welcome, son Frithjof, I have looked for thee to return. For power misled into violence is sure to come to its senses at last and unite with gentleness, if the man's nature but be noble. Thou wouldst atone and be reconciled. Knowest thou the meaning of these words? To atone and be reconciled is to rise after a fall purer, better, than before. We offer sacrifices to the gods and call them atonement. But they are only signs, symbols, not the thing itself. No outward act can take the burden of guilt from thee. A man's atonement is within his own breast. I know of one sacrifice dearer to the gods than rarest incense. It is the surrender of thine own heart's hatred, thy thirst for vengeance. If thou canst not tame these, if thou canst not forgive, then hadst thou better stay away from Balder's fane. Then is thy building of this temple useless. Balder's forgiveness cannot be bought with a few blocks of stone. Thou hatest Bele's sons. Only now has there come news that Helge lies slain in Finland. Halfdan rules alone. Offer him thine hand. Sacrifice to the gods thy wrath. Else is all thy building of the temple vain."

Here Halfdan stepped across the threshold and with timid look which well became his boyish beauty, stood waiting. Slowly Frithjof loosed from his belt the sword and dagger and laid them on the altar, then he approached Halfdan and held out his hand.

"I offer it thee in truest friendship," he said.

Flushing with joy King Halfdan laid his hand in Frithjof's and they two, long parted, joined in a new made bond as firm and strong as their native rocks. Even as they spoke Ingeborg entered in bridal robes. With happy tears she fell upon her brother's breast and he gently placed her in Frithjof's arms. Then was performed the wedding rite, and before Balder's face, now smiling once again, Ingeborg became the bride of the lover of her youth.

FROM THE TOWER WINDOW

Kalevala, Land of Heroes*

Retold from the Kalevala, the National Epic of Finland

COME and hearken to this story, caught from winds and waves and woodlands, from the pastures of the Northland, from the meads of Ka-le-va'la.

In the ancient times it happened in the shining Land of Heroes, that there dwelt an aged graybeard, Wai-na-moi'nen, famous minstrel,—in the vales and on the mountains, through the verdant fields and forests, in the ancient halls and dwellings, ever chanting tales of heroes, singing legends of his people. And so wondrous was his singing that it rippled like the rivers, easy-flowing like the waters, easy-gliding as the snow-shoes, like the ship upon the ocean. Well beloved was Wai-na-moi'nen.

Now it chanced this ancient graybeard, sweetest, best of boasted singers, thought to take a wife unto him, from the dismal, darksome Northland, from the land of cruel winters, from the land of little sunshine, from the land of worthy women. So he ordered to be saddled his fleet-footed steed of magic, and astride that wondrous courser, he began his journey northward. O'er the plains of Kalevala, he went plunging onward, onward,—straight across the blue sea-waters, wetting not the hoofs in running.

But a minstrel less successful, evil-minded You-ka-hai'nen, nursed a grudge against the graybeard, in his heart the worm of envy. He prepared a cruel crossbow, and at breaking of the day-dawn, turned his eyes upon the sunrise,—saw a black cloud on the ocean, something blue upon the waters. This he knew for Wai-na-moi'nen. Quickly now young You-ka-hai'nen, Lapland's vain and evil minstrel, aimed with steady care his crossbow, and with hatred pulled the trigger. Like the lightning flew the arrow, o'er the head of Wai-na-moi'nen, harmless to the upper heavens, scattered all the flock of lamb-clouds. Undiscouraged, You-ka-hai'nen shot again and yet a third time, striking then the graybeard's courser, that light-footed ocean-swimmer.

*This story of the Kalevala is based on Crawford's translation and all the selections used are from that translation.

151

Thereupon wise Wai-na-moi'nen headlong fell upon the waters, plunged beneath the rolling billows, from the saddle of the courser. Then arose a mighty storm-wind, roaring wildly on the waters, bore away old Wai-na-moi'nen far from land upon the billows, washed him seaward on the surges, seaward, seaward, further, further.

Wai-na-moi'nen, old and truthful, swam through all the deep sea-waters, floating like a branch of aspen. Swam six days in summer weather, swam six nights in golden moonlight. Still before him rose the billows, and behind him sky and ocean. So at last he grew disheartened, sad and weary, hoping nothing. Then there came a bird, an eagle, sweeping downward from the heavens. He beheld brave Wai-na-moi'nen struggling there upon the ocean, and was moved with great compassion. Swift he flew unto his rescue. On his back he took the graybeard, bore him safely on his pinions, to the distant shore of Northland, to the dismal Sa-ri-o'la. There he left him, sad and weary, on a cheerless promontory, in his bitter accents weeping, longing for his home and kindred, for his home in Kalevala.

Now the fairest maid in Northland, young and slender Maid of Beauty, on the morning of the morrow, rose before the sun had risen, sheared her six, soft, gentle lambkins, scrubbed the smooth white birchen tables in her mother's low-ceiled dwelling, swept the ground-floor of the stable with a broom of birchen branches, carried in a copper shovel all the sweepings to the meadow. There she lingered by the surges, heard a weeping from the seashore, heard a hero-voice lamenting.

Thereupon she hastened homeward, hastened to her mother's dwelling, told to ancient, toothless Lou'hi, all the story of the wailing. And old Louhi hastening shoreward, pushed her boat into the waters, straightway rowed with lightning swiftness to the weeping Wai-na-moi'nen. Comfort gave she to the minstrel, wailing in a grove of willows. Then she took the hapless hero to her home in dark Poh-yo'la, where she

FROM THE TOWER WINDOW

fed him and revived him, gave him warmth and food and shelter.

And yet ever Wai-na-moi'nen, when his heart grew warm within him, still was longing for his homeland, for his native land and kindred. O, to hear the cuckoo singing, hear the sacred cuckoo calling!

Now the ancient toothless Lou'hi knew her guest for a magician, and she longed with great desiring to possess the magic grist-mill, that same magic grist-mill, Sampo, that could grind unmeasured treasures. So she cried to Wai-na-moi'nen, "I will give to thee my daughter, for thy bride the Maid of Beauty; I will send thee to thy homeland, to thy much-loved Kalevala, there to hear the cuckoo singing, hear the sacred cuckoo calling, if in turn thou forgest for me that same magic grist-mill, Sampo."

Wai-na-moi'nen, much regretting, answered that he could not forge it.

"How to forge the mill I know not. But," he said, "if thou wilt take me to my distant, much-loved homeland, I will send thee Il-ma-ri'nen. Worthy smith is Il-ma-ri'nen. He can forge for thee the Sampo."

So replied the hostess, Lou'hi. "If thou givest me thy promise, then to send me Il-ma-ri'nen, I will let thee leave Poh-yo'la for thy distant home and kindred."

Not delaying, much rejoicing, Wai-na-moi'nen gave his promise. Thereupon the hostess, Lou'hi, harnessed quick a faithful reindeer, hitched him to her sledge of birch-wood, placed within it Wai-na-moi'nen. But before her guest departed, she addressed him thus in warning:

"Do not raise thine eyes to heaven, look not upward on thy journey while the day-star lights thy pathway. If thine eyes be lifted upward ere the evening star has risen, dire misfortune will befall thee, some sad fate will overtake thee."

Thus advised, old Wai-na-moi'nen started fleetly on his journey, hastened homeward happy-hearted.

Fairest daughter of Poh-yo'la,
Glory of the land and water,
Sat upon the bow of heaven,
On its highest arch resplendent,
In a gown of richest fabric,
In a gold and silver air-gown,
Weaving webs of golden texture,
Interlacing threads of silver;
Weaving with a golden shuttle,
With a weaving-comb of silver.
Merry flies the golden shuttle,
From the maiden's nimble fingers.

Came the ancient Wai-na-moi'nen,
Rushing down the highway homeward,
Had not ridden long since starting,
Ridden but a little distance,
When he heard the sky-loom buzzing,
As the maiden plied the shuttle.
Quick the thoughtless Wai-na-moi'nen
Lifts his eyes aloft in wonder,
Looks upon the vault of heaven,
There beholds the bow of beauty,
On the bow the maiden seated,
Beauteous Maiden of the Rainbow,
Glory of the earth and ocean.

In his tone poem *Finlandia*, Sibelius, the greatest musician of Finland, born in 1865, has pictured the beauty of Finland's scenery; the deep woods and long, dark winters; and the Finnish pride of their race.

FROM THE TOWER WINDOW

Wai-na-moi'nen, ancient minstrel, quickly checked his fleet-foot reindeer, thus addressed the charming maiden:

"Come, fair maiden, to my snow-sledge. Come and seat thy-self beside me. Let me take thee to my dwelling, to my home in Ka-le-va'la, there to be my queen and lady."

But the Maid of Beauty answered from her throne amid the heavens that she had no wish to wed him, had no wish to leave her homeland, had no wish to leave her mother, wished to stay a maiden always. All in vain the minstrel begged her. She but answered him with jeering. Could he now do this or that,— setting tasks that even magic scarce could hope to have accomplished, then she might consent to wed him. Nothing daunted, Wai-na-moi'nen, the most skilful of enchanters, every task she set, accomplished, crying always to her, "Maiden, I have done what thou desirest. Come thou then into my snow-sledge."

Lastly said the Maid of Beauty, casting down her magic spindle:

"I will go with that one only that will make me ship or shallop from the splinters of my spindle, from the fragments of my distaff."

Not delaying, Wai-na-moi'nen took at once the wooden splinters, set to work to make the vessel. Full of zeal he plied the hammer, swung the hammer and the hatchet,—till the power of evil, Hi'si, making use of that sharp hatchet, turned aside the axe in falling, cut the knee of Wai-na-moi'nen. From the veins that Hisi severed, there came gushing forth a blood-stream, came a blood-stream, crimson-colored. Nor could then old Wai-na-moi'nen, for the whole of his great knowledge, stay the crimson stream from flowing. Truly, truly had old Lou'hi warned him never to gaze skyward till the evening star had risen, till he could not see the maiden.

Heavy hearted, full of weeping then he climbed into his snow-sledge, and went dashing down the highway seeking some one who could help him. Here and there he asked assistance. There was no one who could heal him. But at last he found a gray-beard dwelling in a little cottage. Wiser he than all the others. When he heard the minstrel's story, from the hearth arose the graybeard, crying thus, "O iron hatchet, tell who taught thee all thy malice, tell who gave to thee thine evil?

> *"Ukko, God of love and mercy,*
> *God and master of the heavens,*
> *Come thou hither, thou art needed,*
> *Come thou quickly I beseech thee,*
> *Lend thy hand to aid thy children,*
> *Touch this wound with healing fingers,*
> *Stop this hero's streaming life-blood,*
> *Bind this wound with tender leaflets,*
> *Mingle with them healing flowers,*
> *Thus to check this crimson current,*
> *Thus to save this great magician.*
> *Save the life of Wai-na-moi'nen."*

Thus at last the blood-stream ended as the magic words were spoken. Then the graybeard brewed a balsam, brewed a magic healing ointment, touched the wounds of Wai-na-moi'nen with the balm of many virtues, speaking words of ancient wisdom:

> *"Do not walk in thine own virtue,*
> *Do not walk in thine own power,*
> *Walk in strength of thy Creator;*
> *Do not speak in thine own wisdom,*
> *Speak with tongue of mighty Ukko.*
> *In my mouth if there be sweetness,*
> *It has come from my Creator;*
> *If my hands are filled with beauty,*
> *All the beauty comes from Ukko."*

Wai-na-moi'nen, old and truthful, felt the help of gracious Ukko, straightway stronger grew in body. Straightway were the wounds united, straight he walked in perfect freedom. Then the ancient Wai-na-moi'nen raised his eyes to high Ju-ma'la, looked with gratitude to heaven, looked on high in joy and gladness, thus addressed all-knowing Ukko:

FROM THE TOWER WINDOW

"O be praised, Thou God of mercy,
Let me praise Thee my Creator,
Since Thou gavest me assistance,
And vouchsafed me Thy protection,
Healed my wounds and stilled mine anguish.
God alone can work perfection,
Give to cause its perfect ending,
Never hand of man can find it.
Never can the hero give it.
Ukko is the only master."

Wai-na-moi'nen, the magician, quickly hitched his fleet-foot reindeer, put his racer to the snow-sledge, straightway sprang upon the cross-seat, snapped his whip adorned with jewels. Like the winds the steed flew onward, made the snow-sledge creak and rattle, made the highway quickly vanish. On he dashed through fen and forest, over marshes, over mountains, over fertile plains and meadows, till he came to Kalevala.

Then began old Wai-na-moi'nen in his secret heart to ponder: "It may now be far from easy to induce good Il-ma-ri'nen to go forth from home and kindred to the dismal darksome Northland. He may never be consenting to fulfill my given promise."

Long he spent in fear and doubting. So he called to aid his magic, and he sang aloft a pine tree, wondrous tall, with branches spreading in the ever-shining sunlight. And he sang again enchanting, sang the moon and Great Bear's starlets to come down from out the heavens, and to hide within the fir-tree, from its emerald branches shining. This accomplished, he went onward to the forge of Il-ma-ri'nen. There he found the mighty blacksmith, wielding his great copper hammer.

"Welcome home, good Wai-na-moi'nen," said the friendly Il-ma-ri'nen. "Where hast thou so long been hiding?"

Spake the minstrel, Wai-na-moi'nen: "I have much to tell thee, brother. I have spent my days in Lapland, all the days of my long absence. There I saw a lovely virgin, fairest maiden of the Northland.

157

"From her temples beams the moonlight
From her breast the gleam of sunshine,
From her forehead shines the rainbow.

Il-ma-ri'nen, worthy brother,
Thou the only skilful blacksmith,
Go and see her wondrous beauty,
See her gold and silver garments,
See her robed in finest raiment,
See her sitting on the rainbow,
Walking on the clouds of purple.

Forge for her the magic Sampo,
Forge the lid in many colors.
Thy reward shall be the virgin,
Thou shalt win this bride of beauty."

But the mighty smith suspected that already Wai-na-moi'nen had made promise in the Northland he should come to forge the Sampo. And he answered shortly, flatly, "I shall never visit Northland, go to dreary Sa-ri-o'la, not for all the maids in Lapland!"

Then alas! did Wai-na-moi'nen turn his wisdom into cunning, fearing lest good Il-ma-ri'nen never could be coaxed to going.

"If thou wilt not, then thou wilt not!" Thus he spake and seemed contented. "But I wish to tell thee, further, of a wonder seen but lately as I crossed the meadows homeward. In the branches of a fir tree I beheld the Great Bear shining, and the moon itself from heaven caught amongst those emerald branches."

"I shall not believe thy story," said the wary Il-ma-ri'nen, "till I see the blooming fir-tree, see the moon and Great Bear's starlets."

This was Wai-na-moi'nen's answer, "Come with me and I will show thee."

Quick they journey to behold it, haste to view the wondrous fir-tree. Il-ma-ri'nen in the tree-top spied the gleam of golden moonlight, spied the shining silver starlight.

FROM THE TOWER WINDOW

"Climb the tree," said Wai-na-moi'nen, "and bring down the moon and starlets."

Il-ma-ri'nen, struck with wonder, senseless, thoughtless, climbed the fir-tree, having neither wit nor judgment, thinking but to seize the treasures. Quick as thought old Wai-na-moi'nen sang again in magic accents, sang a storm wind in the heavens, sang the wild winds into fury.

Now the storm-wind quickly darkens,
Quickly piles the air together,
Makes of air a sailing vessel,
Takes the blacksmith, Il-ma-ri'nen,
Fleetly from the fir tree's branches,
Toward the never pleasant Northland,
Toward the dismal Sa-ri-o'la.
Through the air sailed Il-ma-ri'nen,
Fast and far the hero traveled,
Sweeping onward, sailing northward,
Riding in the track of storm-winds.

Lou'hi, hostess of Poh-yo'la, standing in the open courtyard, quickly spied the hero-stranger, coming thither on the storm-wind.

"Who art thou," she cried, "of heroes?"

Spake the hero then in answer, "Who am I but Il-ma-ri'nen,— I the skilful smith and artist."

"Il-ma-ri'nen!" cried old Lou'hi. "Long I've waited for thy coming. Long I've waited to receive thee!" And she turned into her dwelling, there to call the Maid of Beauty.

"Come thou fairest of my daughters. Dress thyself in finest raiment, deck thy hair with rarest jewels, for the artist Il-ma-ri'nen hither comes from Ka-le-va'la, here to forge for us the Sampo, magic mill of many treasures."

Now the daughter of the Northland straightway took her choicest raiment,—on her brow a band of copper, round her waist a golden girdle, in her hair the threads of silver. From her dressing room she hastened, full of beauty, full of joyance, there to greet the hero-stranger. Lou'hi, hostess of Poh-yo'la, led her guest unto her dwelling, seated him before her table, gave to him the choicest viands. Then she said to Il-ma-ri'nen:

"Canst thou forge for me the Sampo, hammer out its lid in colors? If thou canst, then to reward thee, I will give to thee my daughter."

Il-ma-ri'nen looked about him, saw the maid of wondrous beauty, and he answered to old Lou'hi, "I will forge for thee the Sampo."

Thereupon he sought a workshop, sought to find the tools to work with. But he found no place for forging, found no tongs and found no hammer.

"Only knaves leave work unfinished, grow discouraged," said the artist, "never heroes, never brave men." And he went on seeking further. On the evening of the third day came a rock within his vision, came a rock of rainbow colors. There the blacksmith, Il-ma-ri'nen, set to work and built his smithy, forged the tools that he had need of, and began to forge the Sampo. First he mixed together metals, put the mixture in the caldron, laid it deep within the furnace, called the hirelings to the forging. Soon the fire leapt through the windows, through the door the sparks flew upward, clouds of smoke arose to heaven, clouds of black smoke, circling, rolling. On the third night Il-ma-ri'nen, bending low to view his metals, on the bottom of the furnace, saw the magic Sampo rising. Quick with tongs he seized the mixture,

FROM THE TOWER WINDOW

laid it down upon the anvil, beat it, skilful, with the hammer, forged at last the magic Sampo.

Wild rejoiced the old dame, Lou'hi, took from him the magic grist-mill, found it could in truth grind treasures. Then she bore it off in triumph, hid it in a place of safety.

But, full modest, Il-ma-ri'nen went to seek the Maid of Beauty.

"Wilt thou come with me?" he asked her, "be my queen, O fairest maiden? I have forged for thee the Sampo, forged the lid in many colors."

Northland's fair and lovely daughter saw the artist stand before her, saw him young and strong and handsome. In her heart was secret liking, yet she answered shyly, coyly, "I shall never leave my mother, leave Poh-yo'la's fens and forests, leave my native fields and woodlands."

Il-ma-ri'nen, disappointed, yielded up his dearest wishes, turned away to leave the country, heavy-hearted, empty-handed. Lou'hi gave him every comfort, placed him in a boat of copper, made the North wind guide him homeward. Thus the skilful Il-ma-ri'nen reached again his native country.

Straightway Wai-na-moi'nen asked him, "Didst thou forge the magic Sampo?"

Spake the artist Il-ma-ri'nen, "Yea I forged the magic Sampo, forged the lid in many colors. Lou'hi has the wondrous Sampo. I have not the Bride of Beauty."

Then did ancient Wai-na-moi'nen think within him, "Now the

blacksmith has had every chance to win her, fairy maiden of the rainbow. And since he has failed to lead her to the halls of Kalevala, why may I not now attempt it, now attempt again to win her?" So he decked a magic vessel, painted it in blue and scarlet, trimmed in gold the ship's forecastle, decked the prow in molten silver, made the sails of finest linen,—sails of blue and white and scarlet. Wai-na-moi'nen the magician stepped aboard his magic vessel, steered the bark across the waters, sailing toward the dark Poh-yo'la.

But good Il-ma-ri'nen's sister saw the magic ship departing, hastened off and told her brother, told of Wai-na-moi'nen's going. Il-ma-ri'nen then, the blacksmith, bathed his head to flaxen whiteness, made his cheeks look fresh and ruddy, laved his eyes until they sparkled like the moonlight on the waters. Next he donned his finest raiment, donned his splendid silken stockings, and his shoes of marten-leather, donned a vest of sky-blue color, and his scarlet colored trousers, donned a coat with scarlet trimming and a red shawl trimmed in ermine. Then he wrapped about his body a great fur coat made of seal skin, fastened with a thousand buttons and adorned with countless jewels. On his hands he drew his gauntlets, with their splendid golden wristlets, on his head of many ringlets, put the finest cap in Northland.

Last he bade a trusty servant take the fleetest of his coursers, hitch him to his sledge of magic, place six cuckoos on the breakboard that should sit there, singing, calling,—on the cross bars seven blue-birds, richly colored, ever-singing. Straightway then the trusty servant did as he had been commanded, and the artist Il-ma-ri'nen stepped into his sledge of magic. O'er his knees he drew the bear-skin and the finest robes of marten, called then earnestly to Ukko, "God protect my magic snow sledge, be my safeguard on the journey."

Fast and faster flew the fleet-foot, down the curving snow-capped sea-coast, o'er the alder hills and mountains, through the

FROM THE TOWER WINDOW

sand and falling snow flakes, bluebirds singing, cuckoos calling. Il-ma-ri'nen looked to seaward for old Wai-na-moi'nen's vessel. So at last he overtook it and thus hailed the ancient minstrel:

"O thou ancient Wai-na-moi'nen, let us woo in peace the maiden, fairest daughter of the Northland. Let each labor long to win her. Let her wed the one she chooses."

Wai-na-moi'nen then made answer: "I agree to thy proposal. Let us woo in peace the maiden, not by force or faithless measures. Let her follow him she chooses. Let the unsuccessful suitor harbor neither wrath nor envy."

Thus agreeing, on they journeyed.

Now the hostess of the Northland saw the splendid ship approaching, at the helm the ancient hero,—saw the sledge approaching likewise, cuckoos calling, blue-birds singing, in the sledge the proud young hero. And she hurried to her daughter, urging, "Hither come two suitors. One will offer countless treasure,—that the ancient Wai-na-moi'nen. He, the younger, Il-ma-ri'nen, cometh hither empty-handed. Choose thou then the man of treasures."

But the maiden made this answer, "I will wed no man for treasures. For his worth I'll choose a husband."

And when Wai-na-moi'nen landed, pulled his gaily colored vessel from the waves upon the sea-shore, hastened to the maiden, saying, "Be my bride and life companion," she made answer, shortly, surely, "I will never wed thee, greybeard!"

O, alas for Wai-na-moi'nen! Well for him had he not doubted, feared to trust the blacksmith's friendship, changed his wisdom into cunning, tricked his friend into the tree-top, raised the storm that sent him northward. For when Il-ma-ri'nen sought her, sought again the Rainbow Maiden, spite of Lou'hi's opposition, raising obstacles to hinder, it was he the Maid of Beauty chose at last to be her husband, yielding with her maiden sweetness to the strength of his bold manhood.

163

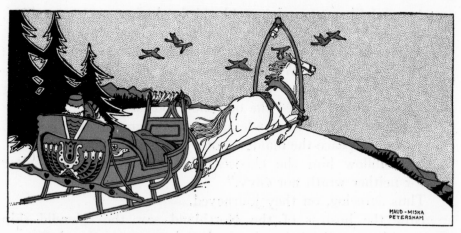

"Il-ma-ri'nen, I will wed thee."

So the ancient Wai-na-moi'nen lost the maiden he had sued for, and he knew, the wise and truthful, he had well deserved to lose her.

Long prepared they for the wedding in Poh-yo'la's halls and chambers,—finest linen on the tables, softest fur upon the benches, birchen flooring scrubbed to whiteness, all the rooms in perfect order. Then came young lads from the village, merry maidens from the hamlets. Thus the wedding guests assembled. Then the ancient Wai-na-moi'nen, keeping well his faithful promise, feeling neither wrath nor envy, sang the joy of all assembled, to the pleasure of the evening, to the merriment of maidens, to the happiness of heroes. Thus he sang, wise Wai-na-moi'nen:

"Grant, O Ukko, my Creator,
God of love and truth and justice,
Grant thy blessing on our feasting.
Bless this company assembled,
For the good of Sa-ri-o'la,
For the happiness of Northland,—
That we may recall with pleasure
Il-ma-ri'nen's magic marriage
To the Maiden of the Rainbow,
Snow-white virgin of the Northland."

FROM THE TOWER WINDOW
As You Like It*
TOLD FROM THE PLAY BY WILLIAM SHAKESPEARE

IN OLD days in France, an ambitious man by the name of
Frederick, secretly gained great power in the province where
his brother was duke. In time, he became so powerful that he drove
his brother from the palace, and wrongfully reigned in his stead.

The banished Duke, driven thus from all his worldly possessions, went to live in the forest of Arden; and many merry men
went with him. There, beneath the great trees beside the brawling
brooks, they lived like Robin Hood, a gay and care-free life as in
that golden age when all the world was young.

The old Duke often said, "Are not these woods more free from
peril than the envious court? When, with icy fang, the winter
wind doth blow—although I shrink with cold—I smile and say
this is at least no flattery. Sweet are the uses of adversity, which
like the toad ugly and venomous, wears yet a precious jewel in its
head." Thus did the Duke find tongues in trees, books in the
running brooks, sermons in stones, and good in everything.

Now the banished Duke had an only daughter named Rosalind whom Duke Frederick had kept at court as companion to
his own daughter, Celia. The two girls, from their childhood,
had loved each other dearly. One day they were walking on the
lawn accompanied by Touchstone, the jester, when they chanced
to meet a courtier just come from a wrestling match. Charles,
an enormous wrestler, had wrestled with three brothers and left
them all half-dead.

"But another youth insists on fighting Charles," said the
courtier. "They are coming here. Stay, and you'll see good sport."

" 'Tis the first time ever I heard that breaking of ribs was
sport for ladies," said Touchstone.

With a mighty flourish of trumpets Duke Frederick and his
attendants soon approached the spot, accompanied by the huge
wrestler and a slight-appearing young man.

*Songs in *As You Like It*, set to music, are "Blow, Blow, Thou Winter Wind" and "Under the Greenwood Tree"
by Dr. Arne (1710-1778); "What Shall He Have Who Killed the Deer," by Sir Henry Bishop (1786-1855).

"How now, daughter and cousin," cried the Duke, "are you crept hither to see the wrestling? You will take little delight in it, there are such odds against this young man. He is young and inexperienced. Speak to him, ladies, and see if you cannot dissuade him from the match." Summoning the young stranger, the Duke left him with the ladies.

"Sir," cried Celia, "we pray you, give over this attempt."

"Your reputation shall not suffer thereby," urged Rosalind, "for we will beg the Duke that he forbid the match to go forward."

"Guilty I am to deny so fair and excellent ladies anything they ask," said the youth, "but, if I am killed, there is only one dead that is willing to die. I have no one to lament me."

"May the little strength I have, be with you," cried Rosalind.

"May your heart's desires come true!" said Celia.

The wrestling match began, but, to the amazement of all, Orlando showed such skill that he threw Charles again and again till the boastful bully lay speechless, unable to rise or move.

M.S.
HURFORD.

FROM THE TOWER WINDOW

Shouts of approval arose and the Duke called the stranger to him, "Young man," he asked, "what is thy name?"

"Orlando," said the youth, "son of Sir Rowland de Boys!"

On hearing that name, Duke Frederick frowned. "I would thou hadst been son to some other man," he said. "I did find thy father mine enemy." And off he went in a rage.

"My father loved Sir Rowland as his soul," cried Rosalind.

"Gentle cousin, let us go thank him and encourage him," said Celia. "My father's envious disposition sticks me at my heart!"

Summoning Orlando to her, Rosalind gave him a chain from her neck. "Wear this for me," she said.

Struck speechless by her beauty, Orlando could say nothing, but as the girls walked away, he asked a passer-by, "Who is yon beautiful maid?"

"'Tis Rosalind, daughter of the banished Duke," the man replied.

"Oh, heavenly Rosalind," Orlando cried.

"My father loved his father dearly," Rosalind said to Celia.

"And, therefore, does it follow that you should love his son dearly?" Celia teased. "By this kind of chase, I should hate him; for my father hated his father dearly, yet I hate not Orlando."

"No faith, hate him not, for my sake!" cried Rosalind.

But, even as the girls were talking, Duke Frederick came upon them. The sight of Orlando had reminded him of the many friends his brother still had in the land. Now long-repressed fear of Rosalind, whose goodness made people love her and remember her banished father, broke loose in a frenzy in Duke Frederick's heart. He ordered her to leave the palace. Celia interrupted, meaning to plead for her cousin, but Frederick cried angrily, "Thou art a fool to plead for her, for thou wilt show more bright and virtuous when she is gone. The doom I have passed will not be changed. She is banished from the court!"

So Celia determined that she would flee with her cousin to seek out Rosalind's father. That they might more safely travel through

rough, unsettled country where robbers might well lurk, Rosalind
dressed as a man while Celia donned poor clothes as if she were a
country maid and stained her face deep brown. Then, taking
their good friend, Touchstone, the girls stole by night from the
palace. Heading toward the forest, they walked many weary miles.
Rosalind was now called by the boy's name, Ganymede, and Celia,
as a country lass, called herself Aliena. With her manly cloth-
ing, Rosalind appeared to have put on manly courage; and,
through the many hardships, she cheered the gentler Celia. But,
when at last they reached the lonely outskirts of the forest knowing not where to seek the Duke, all three were quite worn out.

"I could find it in my heart to disgrace my man's apparel and
cry like a woman," said Rosalind.

"I can go no further," cried Celia, sinking on the grass.

They were sitting in deep discouragement when two shepherds
chanced to pass, an old man and a young one, for, on the fringe
of the forest lay rolling green pasture-land dotted with white
flocks of sheep. The younger man was complaining that some
young maid named Phebe would have none of his wooing. Phebe!
Phebe! Phebe! He talked of nothing but Phebe. And with a
thousand sighs, he left the older shepherd and vanished over the hill.

"I pray you, ask yonder man for food," cried Celia.

"Good-even to you, friend!" Rosalind called to the older shepherd.
"Cans't thou take three weary souls where we may rest and eat?"

"Fair sir," answered the shepherd, "I but work for another.
I do not own the sheep I tend; and now my master, having put
his flocks and sheepcote up for sale, has left the neighborhood."

"Ah," cried Rosalind eagerly, "if the farm is for sale, we will
buy it! You shall be manager of the place."

The man, whose name was Corin, agreed at once to her plan.
He led the three to a cottage with a graceful roof of thatch, beside
a murmuring stream. There, amid the green meadows on the edge
of the shadowy forest, Rosalind as Ganymede and Celia as Aliena

FROM THE TOWER WINDOW

settled down to live. They played at being shepherds, following the sheep or wandering in the forest, attended by Corin and Touchstone. And since Rosalind, dressed as a man, appeared a handsome youth, it chanced that Phebe, the maid who so scorned the shepherd lad, Silvius, fell in love at first sight and followed at Rosalind's heels, much to the amusement of Celia and Rosalind.

It was the Spring of the year. All the earth was a-bloom and love was in the air. Wanderers in the forest sang joyously of love.

"It was a lover and his lass,
  With a hey and a ho and a hey nonino,
That o'er the green cornfield did pass,
  In the springtime, the only pretty ring time,
When birds do sing, hey-ding-a-ding-ding,
  Sweet lovers love the spring."

So Phebe sighed for Ganymede, Silvius sighed for Phebe, and Rosalind sighed for Orlando. Even Touchstone, the jester, found a snub-nosed goat-girl to whom he could make love.

One day in the woods, what did Rosalind find but her own name carved on a tree and beneath it was this verse:

"From the East to western Ind,
  No jewel is like Rosalind!"

Who could have carved that name? Rosalind was a-flutter. And, Celia coming home, brought a verse she had found fastened on a tree. Archly she told Rosalind she had just seen Orlando. Rosalind was all eagerness. Orlando in the woods!

Hard had been the fortune that had brought Orlando to the forest. Years ago his father had died, leaving him to the care of his older brother Oliver. But the youth was too strong and charming to please his envious brother. Jealous of all the affection that everyone showered on Orlando, Oliver saw to it that his brother had no schooling. He kept him at home untaught, with none but servants for friends. "Oliver's horses are better bred than I," Orlando cried in bitterness to the faithful old servant, Adam.

Glowing reports of Orlando's success in the wrestling match so angered the jealous Oliver that he vowed that night to burn the chamber where he slept. Hastening to meet his young master, Adam told him his danger and advised him to flee the place at once.

"I have five-hundred crowns," he said, "saved when I served your father. All this I give to you. Only let me serve you!"

"Good old man!" said Orlando, "how well appears in you the constant service of the old world! You are not for the fashion of these times." And, together, the two set out tramping on and on till they came to the forest of Arden.

"Oh, my dear master," cried Adam. "I can go no farther! I die for want of food!" And he flung himself down on the grass.

But Orlando picked him up and carried him to shelter under some pleasant trees. Then he went off alone in search of food.

Now the old Duke, just at this time, was sitting in a grassy glade under the forest trees with his friends around him at dinner. They were a merry party, and one of them had just sung:

"Under the greenwood tree
Who loves to lie with me,
And tune his merry note
Unto the sweet bird's throat,
Come hither, come hither, come hither;
Here shall he see
No enemy
But winter and rough weather."

FROM THE TOWER WINDOW

Into this merry scene Orlando burst, desperate.

"Forbear and eat no more! I must have your food!" he cried.

"Art thou thus bold, man, by reason of distress?" asked the Duke. "Or art thou rather a rude despiser of good manners?"

"I almost die for food," Orlando cried. "So let me have it!"

"Sit down and feed, and welcome to our table," said the Duke.

Hearing him speak so gently, Orlando blushed with shame.

"Pardon me, I pray you," he put his sword away. "But, since you are so kind, forbear for a moment to eat. There is a poor old man, oppressed with age and hunger, who has limped many a weary step in pure love after me. Till he be satisfied, I will not touch a bit."

"Go! Find him, and bring him hither!" the Duke replied.

Adam and Orlando joined the Duke's men in the forest; and the Duke was overjoyed to have with him his old friend's son. But Orlando thought only of Rosalind. He carved her name on trees and wrote love-sonnets to her. And so it chanced in time, he wandered on the very spot where she and Celia stood talking.

"Forester, do you hear me?" Rosalind cried to him saucily.

"I hear you very well," said Orlando, thinking her a boy.

"I pray you what is't o'clock?" demanded Rosalind.

"You should ask me what time of day it is," said Orlando. "There's no clock in the forest."

"Then there is no true lover in the forest," Rosalind jested, "else sighing every minute and groaning every hour would detect the lazy foot of time as well as a clock!"

Thus she drew the young man into merry conversation, until she could introduce herself as Ganymede, the shepherd lad. In time she spoke jokingly of some half-crazy lover who spoiled the trees by carving the name of Rosalind in their bark.

"If I could find this lover, I'd cure him of his love," she cried.

Straightway Orlando confessed that he was that same fond lover. Then Ganymede guaranteed to cure Orlando's love if he would come every day to the sheepcote. Ganymede would pretend to be Rosalind and Orlando must whisper to him all the sweet nothings and lover's words he would like to say to his sweetheart.

"Then I will imitate all the fantastic ways of ladies to their lovers," Ganymede continued, "until I make you ashamed with all my foolish whimsies of loving such a creature!"

It seemed a good joke to Orlando. His loneliness was relieved at thought of pouring out even to another youth, all the fond words and fine compliments he meant for Rosalind. And so much did Rosalind enjoy hearing her lover tell every day how deeply he loved her that she did not seek out her father. She contented herself with learning that he was well and happy.

Meantime, Orlando's brother, in a rage at his escape had set out to pursue him. He had walked on and on until, in utter weariness, he lay down to sleep in the grass. Orlando chanced to find him as a snake creeping out of the bushes was just about to destroy him. Frightened by Orlando's approach, the serpent glided away. Then the young man perceived a lioness crouched to spring. At the same time, he saw that the man in such danger, was Oliver, his brother, who had said he would burn him alive. For a moment, the young man wavered. Anger surged in his throat. Why not leave Oliver there, a prey to this wild beast? But, almost before he knew it, Orlando drew his sword.

A terrible struggle followed. The lioness clawed him fiercely, but in the end he slew her. Oliver awoke to find that this young brother whom he had so mistreated, had risked his life to save him and been wounded in the struggle. Struck to the heart at sight of such ill-deserved devotion, Oliver felt something hard within him melt in sudden repentance. With tears of a hard man softened, he besought pardon for the wrongs he had done him; and Orlando, deeply rejoicing, forgave his elder brother.

But the wound in Orlando's arm made him too weak to pay his accustomed visit to Ganymede. He sent his brother instead.

FROM THE TOWER WINDOW

Finding at the sheepcote a youth and maid in shepherd's garments, Oliver told them of Orlando's courage and how he was that brother who had so misused the youth. His very evident sorrow for the wrongs he had done, struck Celia with warm compassion. Love glowed in her heart and Oliver, as suddenly perceiving the depth of her sympathy, fell in love with her—though he thought her no more than a shepherd maid as she appeared to be.

Rosalind, however, on hearing how the lioness had wounded her lover, Orlando, disgraced her manly garments by falling in a fainting fit. When she came to herself, she cried, "Tell your brother how well I counterfeited a swoon!"

But Oliver was suspicious. "If you did counterfeit, take a good heart and counterfeit to be a man," he cried. Then he returned to Orlando to pour out the story of his love. He said that he meant to marry the shepherdess, settle his estates on Orlando, and live with his bride as a shepherd in the cottage near the forest.

"Let your wedding be tomorrow," said Orlando, "I will invite the Duke and his friends. How sad it is," he added, as Ganymede just then came anxiously to his side, "to look at happiness through another man's eyes. Tomorrow my brother weds. Would that I, tomorrow, might marry my Rosalind."

"Won't I do for your Rosalind tomorrow?" asked Ganymede.

"Nay, I am through with fancying," Orlando answered sadly.

"Then will I bring her to you by magic," Ganymede promised. "Tomorrow put on your best array, for you shall marry your Rosalind in that same hour when Oliver is married to his love."

"Speakest thou in sober earnest?" cried Orlando.

"By my life, I do!" asserted Ganymede. But just then Phebe and Silvius chanced to pass that way. Perceiving Ganymede, Phebe broke from Silvius to pour out her love as before.

"Pray you, no more of this," cried Ganymede, impatient. "Meet me tomorrow and I'll marry you if ever I marry woman."

Phebe was delighted. "I'll not fail you!" she promised.

And so on the following morning Orlando, Silvius, Phebe, Oliver and his shepherdess, even Touchstone and his goat-girl, Audrey, all gathered in the glade where the Duke was holding court.

Suddenly Ganymede appeared. "If I bring in your Rosalind," she asked the Duke, "will you bestow her on Orlando?"

"Aye, that I will," said the Duke.

"And you'll wed me if I be willing?" Ganymede asked Phebe.

"That will I, should I die the hour after," vowed Phebe.

"But if I refuse, you'll give yourself to this shepherd?"

"So is the bargain," Phebe agreed. Accordingly, Ganymede and Aliena vanished into the forest. Ganymede donned woman's clothes and Aliena, removing the dye from her skin, dressed herself in rich garments which she had brought from the palace. Then they appeared again, coming from the forest greenery, two as lovely maidens as could gladden the eyes of man.

"If there be truth in sight, you are my daughter," cried the Duke, extending his arms toward Rosalind.

"If there be truth in sight, you are my Rosalind," cried Orlando.

"If sight and shape be true, why then, my love, *adieu!*" cried Phebe, turning for comfort to her once-scorned Silvius.

With joy then all the weddings were duly celebrated. It was a great feast of happiness. And to make their joy complete, a man arrived at that moment with a message from Duke Frederick. Frederick, in a towering rage at learning of his daughter's flight, had set out for the Forest of Arden, to seize his brother and his followers. But, on the outskirts of the woods, he had met an old hermit living alone in those wilds. The old man had talked so earnestly of good and evil, right and wrong that Frederick had repented of his wickedness. He therefore sent word to his brother that he would restore the dukedom to its rightful owner. He would enter a monastery and spend the rest of his days righting the wrongs he had done. Great was the joy of all at hearing this happy news, and, in a round of merriment, this tale ends as you like it.

FROM THE TOWER WINDOW

The Exile of Rama

Retold from The Ramayana, the Sacred Poem of India

IN THE midst of the pleasant plain, above the waving green of mango trees, arose the walls and stately towers, the gilded turrets, battlements and spires of fair A-yod'hya, ancient capital of King Das-a-ra'tha and the children of the Sun. Now this great King had led a life of virtue and of valor; yet, though he had three Queens, he had no son to follow him on the throne. So when his years were many, he besought of Heaven a worthy heir to take his place, to rule his people wisely and guard them well. In answer to his prayer there came not one fine son, but four,—Ra'ma, eldest born, son of the Queen Kau-sal'ya, a babe as lovely as a star, so bright that every torch grew dim before him in the chamber of the Queen; Bha'rat, the second son, beautiful and meek and mild, child of the Queen Kai-key'i; and Laksh'-man and his twin brother, sons of the youngest Queen.

Nursed with care, these babes grew into fair, strong youths, filling their father's heart with joy, and he lived in such sweet comradeship with them that he seemed no father but an elder brother to them all. Modest were the princes and in them all the virtues blended. They loved each other as brothers ever should, and roamed the palace grounds together in sweet accord, Rama and Lakshman always side by side. Each prince rendered unto the other's mother such reverence and affection as to his own, and not one of all three Queens but loved the sons of her sister-consorts as dearly as her own.

So the father's bosom glowed with joy and pride for the rare virtues of his sons and the love they showed to one another. But best and noblest of the four, lord of all virtues, in whom all peerless graces dwelt, the King's chief glory was his eldest child, young Rama.

175

For he was gallant, beautiful and strong,
Void of all envy and the thought of wrong.
With gentle grace to man and child he spoke,
Nor could the churl his harsh reply provoke.
He paid due honor to the good and sage,
Renowned for virtue and revered for age.
Just, pure, and prudent, full of tender ruth,
The foe of falsehood and the friend of truth;
Kind, slow to anger, prompt at misery's call,
He loved the people and was loved of all.

The years passed by for those four brothers and their father and mothers in joy and happiness, and Rama, through strong courage, won to wife the fairest maid beneath the heavens, sweet Si'ta, Rose of Women, with whom he lived in tenderest affection.

Then came a time when there arose in the monarch's breast a longing to lay aside the duties he had borne so long, and make his beloved Rama regent-heir, giving over to his hands the reins of government. When he made known his wish unto the people, there arose from all such shouts of loud acclaim as shook the very palace with a storm of sound. How often had Prince Rama, passing through the ample city streets upon his stately elephant or in his gold-decked chariot, bent to greet the townsmen as beloved friends, asking how each one fared, how thrived his wife and babes and servants. And so those townsmen loved him with exceeding great devotion. Joyous preparations were begun at once to consecrate Lord Rama regent in his father's stead.

But now, though Rama was his father's best beloved son, the lovely Queen Kai-key'i, mother of Bharat, was the King's most cherished wife. A princely palace he had built this favorite Queen, with many a little balcony that overhung fair gardens, where trees were ever glowing with fruit, where all was bright with vivid oriental flowers, and gay flamingoes stalked midst swans

*The selections from The Ramayana used in this story are from the translation by Ralph T. A. Griffith.

and cranes and peacocks spreading gorgeous jewelled trains. From the roof of this splendid palace, Kai-key'i's little hunchbacked maid looked out over all the town, and saw its temples gleaming white, its palaces and gay bazaars arrayed as if for holiday, with pennons flying in the scented air, and concert of glad music rising on the breeze. Learning that the cause of all this festive array was that Prince Rama, son of Queen Kau-sal'ya, was to be proclaimed the regent-heir, she ran in furious haste to where her mistress lay asleep.

"Up, up, my Queen! Arise!" she cried. "Great peril threatens thee. Thy lord will make Prince Rama regent over all the land! Then will all wealth and honor be given to Queen Kau-sal'ya, and thou wilt be despised. All power will be Prince Rama's, and how sad will be the fate of thy dear son, Prince Bharat!"

But Kai-key'i only rose, delighted with the news.

"I rejoice that Rama shares his father's throne!" she cried. "Kau-sal'ya's son is even as dear to me as mine own child. He

hath been ever good and kind, meek to his mother and meeker still to me. What difference though he rule? There is no cause to fear. His brethren are as dear to him as his own soul."

But the crook-backed maid, burning with jealous envy, so urged her point that at the last she poisoned Queen Kai-key'i's mind, and there flamed within her but one single thought, to make the King, her husband, name her son, Prince Bharat, regent in the place of Rama, and send beloved Rama into exile in the woods. Then the evil-minded maid, eager to work her will, reminded the jealous Queen how she once tenderly nursed her husband of a wound received in battle and he, out of love and gratitude, had sworn to grant her any two requests. A vow so deeply sacred, no true Hindu would ever dare to break.

"Ask that he name thy Bharat regent," said the maid, "and send Rama into exile far within the woods."

Now Prince Bharat was from home just then, attending at an uncle's court, and his mother took upon herself alone the full responsibility for his fate. Casting aside her splendid robes and jewels, she dressed herself in mourning garments and threw herself upon the floor in a mean and wretched little chamber, there awaiting her husband in pretended agony and woe.

Slow and majestic as the moon gliding in glory across the calm fields of the autumn sky, passed King Das-a-ra'tha to his darling's palace. Not finding her awaiting him at the usual place, where she was wont to gladden his eyes by sight of her at that hour, he anxiously sought news of her from her maids. Being by them informed where she had taken herself, he passed on to the mean and wretched chamber, and there found her prostrate on the ground. Anxious to soothe her grief, he knelt beside her and tried many a kind caress, coaxing her to tell him what moved her to such sorrow. Seizing her chance, the Queen reminded him of his promise long since given when she had nursed him of his wound, and bade him now swear to grant her two

FROM THE TOWER WINDOW

requests. Betrayed by his great love, the King leapt like a deer into the snare she laid. With a fond smile, he placed his hand beneath his darling's head and raised her up, then solemnly swore to grant her any two requests, reminding her that no one on the earth was dearer to him than she, save only Rama.

"This solemn pomp that thou hast begun in Rama's honor," she cried, "give over to Bharat! Consecrate my son and send thy Rama, banished for fourteen years, into the distant forests."

Struck dumb with horror at her words, the King spoke not a word at first, the while there dawned upon him all the meaning of the boon she asked—the deep-laid scheme by which she had entrapped him. Then in his indignation he burst forth:

"The world may live without the sun as well as I without my Rama! Take Rama from me and what is life then worth to me? How couldst thou scheme so foul a plot? What has my Rama ever done to thee? Hast thou not often held him as a babe upon thy knee and when he smiled, sworn he was dear to thee as thine own son? Has he not ever shown thee sonlike love and sweet obedience? O wife, have mercy on my bitter cry. Take all my treasures but leave my Rama here with me!"

No thrill of pity stirred the soul of that envy-hardened queen. She still claimed stubbornly fulfilment of the oath. The whole long dreary night the unhappy King spent in entreaty, searching out the way to touch her heart. He could not move her from her purpose. So dawned the morning of the day that had been set aside for Rama's consecration, and that noble youth, summoned from his beloved Sita's side to seek his father, entered the chamber where the King and Queen Kai-key'i lingered. Reverently Rama bowed to greet his royal sire, and then as reverent, did obeisance at Kai-key'i's feet. The King with downcast eyes, that brimmed with tears, could only murmur, "Rama!" and then say no more. The youth beholding what a change the night had wrought in his dear father, and seeing him thus weeping

179

and unstrung, was pierced with sorrow, and turning to Kai-key'i asked her courteously the cause for such a change. That greedy dame, lost now to shame, told the whole matter to the Prince, how the King, his father, had taken most solemn oath to grant her two requests, yet now would shamefully refuse to keep his word because the boons she asked meant that her Bharat should be regent and he, Rama, sent off for fourteen years to exile.

No angry word, no sharp reproof passed Rama's gentle lips. At once he said:

"Fear not, O lady, my father's faith shall never be pledged in vain. If he hath promised I will go. Heralds shall summon Bharat home to take my place as regent, and I will don the hermit's garb and fare forth to the forest. One duty I hold above all others—that a son should ever serve and be obedient to his father."

Then he gently stooped to comfort his beloved father, who in speechless woe had heard his words. With reverent farewell he left the bower where Queen Kai-key'i sat exulting in her triumph, and went to pay one last sad visit to his own beloved mother. As he passed along the streets, he saw the signs of joy, no more for him, and all the sacred vessels arranged for that great day, the golden chalices, whose water poured upon his head would have ordained him lord. He saw and did not turn his eye away. His glance betrayed no anguish, his foot no haste. Still on his brow, though his high hopes were dead, shone that great glory that was all his own.

He found his mother in linen robes of purest white, intent on holy rites, for she was of more serious mood than lotus-eyed Kai-key'i. But when she heard his news, how hope of being regent was no more for him, but exile in the distant forest in its place, she wept in black despair and none could comfort her. Then came the faithful brother, Lakshman, devoted to Prince Rama, and in anger cried that he would set his Rama on the throne by force if Rama would permit, for what had come to pass

FROM THE TOWER WINDOW

was all unfair. With streaming eyes the mother too begged Rama to give heed to Lakshman's counsel.

"Forgive me, Mother," said the hero gently. "I have no power to disobey my father. See me at thy honored feet and give me now thy blessing, for I needs must go."

So forced at last, Kau-sal'ya let him go.

"May virtue be thy sure defence!" she cried. "Thy tender love and meek obedience, like a mystic charm, will arm thy soul, my Rama! Go forth my son, my pride and glory, go!"

Then Rama fell upon his knees before her, pressed her dear feet and said his last farewell. With Lakshman still beside him, he turned his anxious steps toward his own home. The hardest trial of all remained before him still, to take his leave of his beloved Sita. As he passed through his stately halls, his eye was drooping and his brow was overcast. Wont as he was to curb each passion with a firm control, he yet could scarcely bear within his own strong bosom the load of anguish that was heavy there. Quick to trace the sorrow on his face, sweet Sita cried:

"What ails thee, O my lord? This happy day
Should see thee joyful. All but thou are gay.
Why does no royal canopy, like foam
For its white beauty, shade thee to thy home?
Where are the tuneful bards thy deeds to sing?
Where are the fans that wave before the king?
Why doth the city send no merry throng
To bring thee home with melody and song?
Why doth no gilded car thy triumph lead,
With four brave horses of the swiftest breed;
No favored elephant precede the crowd
Like a black mountain or a thunder-cloud;
No herald march in front of thee to hold
The precious burthen of thy throne of gold?
If thou be King, ordained this day, then why
This sorry plight, pale cheek and gloomy eye?"

Thus Sita questioned in her wild suspense and Rama told her gently all the tale, how there was no anointing now for him, how,

181

forced by duty's higher law, he must go forth to exile, leaving her and all he loved behind.

"Be firm and strong, dear wife, when I am gone," he said, "and ever serve with tender care the King, my father. Be dutiful unto Bharat, too, since he will rule, and never vex him; cheer my beloved mother, and show love to all the consort-queens— they are my mothers even as mine own. Be ever gentle, humble and content."

But Sita answered, modest and yet firm, "The wife's fit place is by the husband's side. I spurn the terrace and the pleasant seat at ease in palaces when thou must face the hardships of the woods. If thou wilt go, then I go too. No heaven is anywhere for me, if thou art gone."

Lost in deep thought, the hero stood, yet still he feared to lead this tender flower into the rough and fearsome forest.

"Life in the woods is naught but grief and pain," he urged. "There the lion roars in his rocky cave, the tiger stalks abroad, and everywhere wild beasts in ambush lie. Within the streams ferocious crocodiles lie hid, and oft wild elephants rush forth, while on the gale comes borne the wolf's long howl. The homeless wretch, clad in a rough and untrimmed coat of bark, must wander through a wilderness of sand and thorn and sleep upon the ground. Enough, dear love. A life like that is not for thee. Stay home, my Sita, and be happy here."

But Sita spoke once more with weeping eyes: "The woe, the terror, all the toil and pain will but be joy to me, joined with thy love. O let me go! Whate'er I may endure, following thee, will only make my soul more pure. Fear not for me! O my Rama, let me go!"

And with a bitter cry she flung her arms round Rama's neck and clung there till he gave her leave to go.

"I knew not, love, the strength of thy fond heart," he said. "Naught now shall ever part me from my wife."

FROM THE TOWER WINDOW

Then Lakshman's eyes began to overflow with generous tears. Fondly caressing his brother's feet he said, "If thy purpose then is changeless, I too will follow thee nor ever leave thee."

Rama sought in vain to urge his brother to remain behind. That true and faithful friend would not yield his intent. So the royal three, Rama, and his true wife, Sita, and Lakshman, faithful to the end, walked for the last time to the palace, to see the aged King. Through crowds that filled each street and balcony, each portico and roof, they passed, and pity moved the hearts of all to see the highborn princess and the kingly youths so humbly walking in the way. Loud from their loving hearts the people called to Rama to remain and be their King. Firm in duty, he heeded not their words but passed on to the palace.

Surrounded by his queens and ladies of his court, the King stood waiting. When his two sons with Sita came within the hall, the wretched father fell prostrate to the ground, and all the mighty hall was rent by one great wail. Mid the silver sound of tinkling ornaments that bound their wrists, a thousand women in one wild lament cried, "Rama! Rama!"

Still no complaint the noble Rama made. He comforted his father and spoke soothingly to all.

"Let chariots, elephants, horsemen, all my treasures follow in Lord Rama's train to ease his exile!" cried the King.

But Rama answered: "All that—the host, the riches, and the pomp would be quite useless to me, sire. For I have left the world and all its false desires, its pride and cares behind. I shall lead within the wilderness the hermit's life of sweet simplicity."

Then Queen Kai-key'i, with unblushing brow, handed out with her own hands the rough bark mantles to the three. Removing their fine garments, Rama and Lakshman donned at once the hermit's dress, but tender Sita in her flowing silks, eyed the strange garment trembling. Nestling closer to her Rama's side, she begged him in her soft, low, faltering accents to help her put it on. With his own hands Lord Rama fastened it, but over her silks, not next her tender skin. Then the Rose of Women took her seat in the sun-bright car the King had waiting; Rama and Lakshman sprang in by her side, and bearing with them naught save only a basket bound in hide and a husbandman's hoe, they left the city, crowds following their chariot, weeping and lamenting. Last sight of all, Lord Rama saw his father, grief stricken, on the ground, and with him his sad mother and her train, and his last look of love and grief was in the eyes of that beloved mother.

Riding thus, the exiles came by night where the dark river Jum'ne pours her tributary tide with kissing waves into the Ganges' crystal flood. There beneath a spreading banyan tree they spent the night and in the morning built a raft, by means of which they crossed the sacred stream. From there Lord Rama watched the faithful subjects who had followed him to Ganges, sadly wending homeward on the far bank of the river. Then with Sita bidden always to walk between him and his brother, that they two might guard her from all harm, he plunged into the forest. In single file they marched through the wonderful tropical jungle, amidst a wealth of vivid flowers, beneath huge trees where brilliant birds made music, and chattering monkeys leapt from limb to limb. And so they came at last where that vast mountain Chit-ra-ku'ta, tinged with a thousand dyes, lifts his summit to the sky, while all about him higher peaks ascend. So beautiful was that spot that, beholding it, Lord Rama's soul

FROM THE TOWER WINDOW

was filled with deep content and he cried unto his comrades:

"See waving in the western wind,
The light leaves of the tamarind;
And mark that giant peepul through
Those feathery clumps of tall bamboo.
That depth of shade, that open lawn
Allure the wood-nymph and the fawn;
And, where those grassy glades extend,
The spirits of the air descend,
To while the summer night away
With dalliance and mirth and play.
Look, from the mountain's woody head
Hangs many a stream like silver thread,
Till, gathering strength, each rapid rill
Leaps, lightly laughing, down the hill,
Then, bounding o'er the rocky wall,
Flashes the foamy water-fall."

Thrilled with the joy of that wonderful spot, the exiles went on a little further till below them they saw a beautiful river, a glorious limpid stream. On its shelving bank, their early bathing done, stood a company of hermits lifting reverent hands in prayer.

"There," said Lord Rama, "will we make our home."

So the exiles joined that colony of simple souls, whose days were passed in sacred study, who sought to work not, speak not, think not sin. There Rama and Prince Lakshman built a rustic bower for Sita, and in that spot they three dwelt long in mutual love and tenderness. In the gentle stream sweet Sita often bathed and plucked red lilies for her hair, then in some green and grassy glade she and Lord Rama took their fill of gazing on the landscape, watching now the bright flamingoes with their rosy wings, and now the swans and herons on the stream below, or troops of deer come gently to the banks to drink. Rama and Lakshman gathered fruit for food and brought in trophies of the chase, which Sita with gay cheerfulness prepared and cooked.

Thus in simple joy the time passed by until it chanced one day that one among the hermits brought disturbing news of a great multitude seen marching through the forest toward the hermitage. Climbing quickly to the tipmost top of a giant tree, Lakshman beheld a long procession winding through the woods. In great excitement he descended to the ground and cried:

"O Rama, I doubt not that this is Bharat come to finish his envious mother's work and put thee by force out of his way forever! Beware!"

Gently Lord Rama rebuked his brother, for it was not in his heart ever to think evil of another.

"Nay, my dear Lakshman," he replied. "That cannot be. If Bharat comes at all, he comes to do us good, with some most loving purpose in his heart."

And so when the long train drew near, Lord Rama greeted Bharat with the tenderest affection, while Lakshman stood half scowling and suspicious by. But Bharat flung himself before Lord Rama's feet with bitter tears.

"Dear brother," he said, "on my return from visiting our uncle, how shocked was I to hear what in my absence had been done, how my poor mother, deluded quite, had forced our father to name me regent in thy stead and drive thee into exile. And now, O Rama, out of grief for thee, our father, alas! is dead, thy mother his best comfort in his latest hours. And I, my lord and King, will never take thy place. Return, dear brother, to thy rights and reign in fair A-yod'hya!"

Overcome at first with grief at hearing of his father's death, Lord Rama made no answer, but at last he said:

"Nay, brother, what are pomp and wealth and pride of place? 'Tis virtue only marks the line between the great and good, the low and mean. I promised for full fourteen years to stay in exile. Shall I then break my oath and prove untrue unto my holy promise, when truth is root and spring of every virtue? Misled by false desire for power and might, shall I despise that holy gem of truth, attracted by an earthly prize? Nay, brother! Urge this

FROM THE TOWER WINDOW

plea no more. I still will keep my oath nor leave this forest till the fourteen years are past. Do thou return and act as regent of the realm, and this I promise thee—I will not live my years of banishment in idleness, but will spend them so that they shall shower rich blessings on my people."

In vain Bharat entreated. Rama stood steadfast in his purpose. Then Bharat, bending to embrace his brother's feet, besought of him his golden sandals, crying, "If thou thyself wilt not return and I must be the regent in thy stead, then will I never sit upon thy throne. Thy sandals only shall occupy that royal seat beneath the white umbrella of the King. Bharat will rule in Rama's name."

With utmost generosity and love those brothers said farewell, and the gorgeous train with Bharat at its head, slowly wended once again its way through the forest paths to fair A-yod'hya. And there for fourteen years by Bharat's will, the sandals of Lord Rama occupied the throne beneath the white umbrella, and all men did homage to those sandals, nor was Bharat tempted once within his soul to prove untrue unto his elder brother.

As to Rama in the forest,—he rose up in all the might of noble manhood and sought out, through toil and long and difficult adventure, the source and well-spring of all evil in the world, that impious demon, Ravan, who defied the Lord of Lords, and all the Hosts of Heaven. Him Rama slew, and so, through long hard years of self-forgetful exile, did he bring deliverance to his people. But when the fourteen years were up, he went with Lakshman and sweet Sita, Rose of Women, unto A-yod'hya once again, and there midst loud rejoicings of his people, he took at last his rightful seat upon the golden throne beneath the regal white umbrella that served only for the King.

187

Cuculain, the Irish Hound
Retold from Tales of the Ancient Gaelic Bards

HEN all the world was young and men towered up in elemental hardihood like wind-blown oaks, there dwelt in Ulster, a race of giant heroes, the warriors of the Red Branch. Mighty exceeding, these heroes, and vast the hall where they met in the stronghold of Emain Macha! Lit was that hall by candles, innumerable, tall as spears. Of these colossal heroes was Concobar Mac Nessa, King, and Fergus MacRoy, Champion; yet looked they for one to come in spirit more gigantic still; for so had the long-beard and prophet, Ulster's Arch-Druid foretold.

> *"Yea, he is coming; he draweth nigh,*
> *Verily it is he whom I behold—*
> *The predicted one—the child of many prophecies—*
> *Torch of the valor and chivalry of the North,*
> *A star to shine forever on the forehead of the Gael!"*

Gleaming far and afar, the Oak House of Dun Dalgan, whitewashed and thatched of roof, stood on the height of a hill, above its earthen walls; and there was growing up Se-tan'ta, son of Su-al'tam and of Concobar's sister, Dec-ter'a. The boy had a silver ball and a little ashen hurl-bat; he had a sheaf of toy arrows, a wooden sword and a shield. Hardy and pure of mind, he knew not guile nor baseness, but played along the sands beside the rolling waves. Dressed in his woolen tunic and little scarlet bratta, he sat among bearded men in the great hall of the dun, and hearkened to tales of heroes, and the thrice fifty boys of the boy-troop, who were trained in Concobar's care. And when he was five years old he spake to his mother thus: "I would go to have part in the games with the boy-troop of Emain Macha."

FROM THE TOWER WINDOW

Dectera's face grew pale. "Thou art too young," she said. And she took him from men's society and kept him with the women, always by her side. But little Setanta dreamed,—where lay Emain Macha? Where lay the city of the King? Far, far off and away, over yon mountain-height, Setanta's mother said. The boy took his sheaf of toy javelins, his wooden shield and his hurl-bat, and flinging the ball in the air, he hit it with his hurle, and followed fleet where it fell. "Thy blessing, dear mother!" he cried, stopping beneath her window.

"Win victory and blessings, dear Setanta," she said, but her heart leapt and her tears fell! How soon he was out of sight!

Swiftly Setanta went! With his hurle he urged his ball forward and ran in race with its flight! By night he slept on the mountain beside the heap of stones sacred to the hero of the place; and on the second day he saw far off and shining, the walls of Emain Macha. Slowly he went on now, over the drawbridge, up the hill, up to the great, painted palace. Scarcely dared he set foot in such a holy place. But hark, there fell on his ears gay voices of the boy-troop, who brake from the palace laughing and ran down the wide, smooth lawn to the playfield, and hurling-ground.

189

At sight of them, his heart yearned. He longed to be their friend; yet knew not how they would receive him. Fear strove with hope and love. Solitary he stood, hoping that someone would call him, and bid him take part in the game; but none there called or welcomed. Silently the child wept; he had thought he would be made much of because of his skill in hurling, because he so longed for comrades, and because there was in his heart such a well-spring of loving-kindness. But no one seemed glad of his coming, and he was among these boys of no account at all.

Bitter were his tears. Soon the ball, struck side-ways, bounded near Setanta. Glowing with fire of the game, he followed the bounding ball. Out-running the others, he seized it, and urged it ever forward. Not one of all those boys could get a prod or a stroke, a blow or a shot at the ball! He carried it over the goal!

Then he approached the boy-troop; but he said not: "I ask your protection," for he wist not that such was the custom. So they all set upon him together. They cast their hurl-bats at him. He raised his single toy-staff and warded off the hurlies. They threw their balls and play-spears. He raised his little wooden shield and fended off the blows. Then battle-rage seized upon him, and the champion's light rose from his crown. He scattered fifty king's sons over the ground underneath him! Five of the boy-troop fleeing, dashed in headlong haste 'twixt Fergus MacRoy and King Concobar, where they sat playing chess on the mound-seat; but little Setanta pursued them, springing over the chess-board. Concobar seized the lad. "Hold little boy!" he said, "I see it is not gently that thou dealest with the boy-band!"

"Good reason!" quoth Setanta, "from mother and father I came only to play with them, and they are not good to me!"

"Who art thou?" asked Concobar.

"Little Setanta am I, son of thine own sister!"

"Knewest thou not," said Concobar, "that no boy may join the boy-band unless he first pray their protection?"

FROM THE TOWER WINDOW

"Nay, I knew it not," little Setanta made answer.

"Good now, ye boys," cried Concobar, "protect this little lad!" But when they were gone to their games, Setanta once more rushed amongst them so that they fled through the house, and many were in such case that their nurses and tutors must aid them. And Setanta made them all place themselves beneath his protection, even as but now they had demanded that he ask protection of them. Thus did the little lad when he was but five years old, and thus did he become the leader of the boy-troop, while Fergus became his tutor and loved him as his own son.

Now in the following year, Setanta performed a second deed; for there came then unto Emain a huge man, grim and swarthy, even Culain, the smith, who made weapons for the men of Ulster. He came to Emain Macha to bid Concobar to a feast and then he went back to his dun, noisy with ring of hammers, where sparks from the anvils by night, and the red glare of the furnaces painted far the sky above the barren moor. When the time for the feast was come, the King in his traveling apparel set out for Culain's home, with fifty of his chariot-chiefs, betaking himself to the boy-troop to bid them farewell ere he went. There he saw Setanta outdoing all others in games, and he called the lad to him and said: "Come with us to the feast of Culain." But the lad made answer straightway: "Let me first finish my games." So Concobar gave his consent, and went on his way to the dun.

Now when Culain saw from afar the chariot-chiefs approaching, he called to his men to stop work, to wash them of smoke and sweat, and to put them on clean clothes to receive the heroes of the Red Branch. And Concobar crossed the drawbridge, and Concobar passed the gate, and he clomb to the house of Culain that crowned the height of the dun. Straw and fresh rushes were spread and all began to make merry. Then Culain inquired of Concobar: "Are all thy men arrived?" And Concobar answered "Yea!" for he had forgotten Setanta.

"Now I will unloose my blood-hound!" Culain continued to say, "by day he is kept with three chains and three men at every chain, for the power of hundreds is in him, and he obeys no man save me. Because of our goods and cattle, we loose him every night as soon as the gates are shut."

"Let the ban-dog be loosed," said Concobar. So the dog-chain was taken off the ban-dog, and he made a swift round of the cantred, till he came to the mound whereon he was ever wont to keep guard. There he sat, his head on his paws! Aye, wild, untameable, furious, savage, ferocious, ready for fight was the ban-dog that was there.

Meantime, the games being finished, the little lad, Setanta, set out on the trail of the King, shortening the way with his play-things. But when he drew nigh the dun, the watchdog descried him and bayed, so that in all the countryside was heard the howl of the watch-hound. And he meant not to divide the mouthful he made of the lad, but to swallow him down at a gulp! And the lad had not with him any means of defense, but he seized the hound by the legs and began to wrestle with him.

FROM THE TOWER WINDOW

Within the hall, King Concobar heard the yelp of the ban-dog; and Concobar and his people could not move for fear. They bethought them at once of Setanta and they weened they would never now find the lad alive. As one man they arose, all the renowned men of Ulster. They leapt the palings of the fence. But fast as they all ran, faster than all arrived Fergus; and he lifted the lad to his shoulder and bore him to Concobar. They put him on Concobar's knee and great alarm arose because that the King's sister's son had just been all but slain. But the smith went to look for his hound, and he found that the hound lay dead; and coming again to the hall, he said: "Not luckily for me hast thou come to quaff my ale; for good was the friend thou hast robbed me of, the protection of all our cattle, both afield and at home."

As he spake, unquenchable wrath, earth-born, seethed among the smiths; so they reached for their hammers and tongs, their fire-poles, and bars of brass, while the men of Ulster in answer, straightway sprang to the walls to take down their shields and spears from the pegs where they had hung them ere the feasting began. But little Setanta cried: "Be not angered, O Culain! I slew not thy dog in wantonness, but in defense of my life. I grieve that he is dead. Yet since I needs must kill him, I will pay thee a worthy *eric*, for verily I myself will take the place of thy dog, and nightly guard thy cattle till a hound as worthy be found."

"Well spoken, little lad!" cried Concobar and Culain.

"Well spoken," cried Cathba the Druid, "Henceforth, be thou called not Setanta, but *Cuculain*, the hound of Culain! And the men of Erin and Alba shall hear that name and the mouths of the men of Erin and Alba shall be full of that name!" And thus it was that Setanta came by his second name Cuculain.

Now when Cuculain was seven years old, Concobar agreed that there should be for him the Taking-of-Arms, and from the palace he came, shamefast in sweet humility, but in all the glory of youth. Beautiful was the lad; his comeliness appeared upon him. Bright yellow was his hair with diadem of gold. Hooded tunic of cloth of gold and fair green mantle were on him; and lo, the silver brooch on his breast gleamed so that eyes of men could not look at it for its brightness. The lad came and seated himself between the two feet of Concobar while the King stroked his golden hair. And Concobar bestowed upon him the chariot of the goddess Macha, with its weird and terrible horses, Li'ath Ma'cha, the giant roan, who could make himself large and larger, and the coal-black steed, Black Shangh'lan from dusky haunts of the Night! And Concobar gave Cuculain a shield, with two spears and a sword, the best in all the land, and from the lads of the boy-troop Cuculain chose Laeg of the Black-Hair, to be his charioteer. Wild neighing of immortal steeds, thunderous rumbling of the great war-chariot, and there it came into view, black and gold in color, with glorious twinkling wheels! And Cuculain leapt into the chariot, and Laeg held the glistening reins. Like a hawk swooping down the face of the cliff when the wind is very high, was the rush of those two horses; they overtook birds in their flight! From peak to peak they leapt, thrice round the whole of Ireland, while all that assembly of heroes lifted up voice in a shout!

FROM THE TOWER WINDOW

Now when Cuculain was seventeen, there befell the Cow-raid of Coolney, and Cuculain's most daring deeds. For in those days, Mave, the Queen of Connaught, and King Ailill, her husband, spread their royal bed in Cruachan, the stronghold of Connaught, and such was the pillow-talk that befell betwixt them. Quoth Ailill: "Thou art much better off than the day when I wedded thee!"

"Nay, nay!" quoth Queen Mave. "I was as well off ere ever I saw thee! My fortune is greater than thine!" And thereto they fell to disputing which had the greater possessions. Then were brought to them their iron-wrought vessels, their jugs, their eared-pitchers and pails, their apparel, their bracelets, their rings.

Their numerous flocks of sheep were led in from fields and meads. Their horses and steeds were brought from pastures and from paddocks. Their numerous droves of swine were driven in from the woods, from shelving glens and wolds. All were numbered and found to be equal. Only over the King's cattle was that enormous bull, White-horned, so masterful that in all Connaught no bull durst send forth a low that was louder than a moo in compare with him. And Mave had no bull to equal him, and for all her other treasures, it was as if she owned not a pennyworth, forasmuch as she owned no such bull! Then said to her, her messenger MacRoth, "I know where is a bull that is best and better again in the province of Ulster, in the hundred of Coolney, in the house of Dara, even the Brown Bull of Coolney." And Queen Mave said to her messenger, "Pray Dara to lend me this bull."

So the messenger fared him forth and he offered Dara much land and a chariot which should be of the worth of seven bond-maids. And Dara leapt for joy so that the seams of his flock-bed rent in twain beneath him, and he agreed to send his gigantic Brown Bull to Mave. Then straw and fresh rushes were spread, good food and drink were served and soon were the messengers drunken, so that one began to boast: "It is well for Dara that he granted the bull full willingly, for had he not done so, yet would our Queen have come and taken him by force!" Thereupon Dara was angered and stubbornly cried that now he would never give up the bull. But the Warrior-Queen, hearing of this, cried: "Our messenger spake but truth, for taken by force he shall be!"

So four of the five grand provinces of Erin went to war against Ulster under Ailill and Queen Mave, and they thought to take not only the Brown Bull of Coolney, but all the cattle in Ulster; for there was in those days a spell on all the warriors of the Red Branch. For sin against the goddess Macha, there fell upon them every year during a certain season, a sleep and a confusion, a drunkenness and a babbling, a dreaming and loss of strength.

FROM THE TOWER WINDOW

Cuculain and his father, Sualtam, alone of all grown men were free of the spell in Ulster; and Cuculain alone and unaided guarded the borders of the land. Nor was Fergus there to aid him; for Fergus had quarrelled with Concobar, and Fergus and other good Ulstermen now served the Queen of Connaught.

Mighty were the hosts of Queen Mave in the snow-fall of Winter-beginning! The Queen rode with nine war-chariots, two before, two behind, and two on either side, that the dust of the host might not reach her diadem of gold. And beside her rode her daughter, Finnabair, the Fairbrow, to lure the champions to war. The lead of the way was given to Fergus, and sad was his heart for Cuculain, and he said to the men of Erin: "Beware thou of Cuculain; for thou findest not in Erin a hero that is his peer, nor a lion that is fiercer. Thou findest not one that could equal his age and his growth; his size and his splendor; his dash, his assault, his attack!"

"We make not much import of this Cuculain," quoth Queen Mave, "for they say that his age is but that of a girl to be wed!"

So passed the armies of Mave across the river Shannon, and since the great warriors of Ulster all sat under the spell, they met no outpost, no sentinel; but passed unhindered as they would. And Mave's men found the Brown Bull of Coolney, and brought him back to camp, plunging and careering, pawing and digging up earth. On the fifth day of marching, however, they came upon a young sapling twisted round a pillar stone, and on the hoop was writ in ancient Ogam characters, a challenge from Cuculain. Thereafter death hovered about them, death, and death again. "Cuculain!" they whispered, "destroys us!" When they came to Avon Dia, border-stream of the Red Branch, Queen Mave sent Fergus MacRoy to fetch Cuculain to her. And Fergus embraced Cuculain, and the two wept for joy of their meeting. But when Mave and the Kings of Erin looked upon Cuculain, they were astonished greatly; for his face was smooth as a boy's, and, standing in his leather kilt with a wide battle-girdle of ox-hide reaching from his waist to his armpits, he seemed in sooth to Queen Mave, no bigger than the bulk of a stripling. But Mave agreed with Cuculain that no man should cross the ford until in single combat, Cuculain was overthrown. Thereafter every day there fell a man by Cuculain, and so great did the fame of him grow, that the maidens of Connaught besought the men of Erin to lift them up on their shields above the warriors' shoulders, and the women of Munster clomb on the men to get but a glimpse of the hero.

And King Ailill planned a trick. "Let my fool go forth in my clothes," he said, "taking Finnabair Fairbrow with him. Let him stand too far off to be recognized, and so let him promise Finnabair as bride to this Cuculain, if he but give up the fight!"

Nevertheless, Cuculain recognized the fool and shot a sling-stone at him while the girl fled home alone. And now all the warriors of Erin feared to meet the hero! Ailill planned another trick. Henceforth when he chose a champion, he gave him over-much wine; the Fairbrow was placed at his side; she filled his drinking horn, and gave him a kiss with each draught; she promised to be his bride if he brought back the head of Cuculain. Yet Cuculain killed them all, till none would fight him more.

FROM THE TOWER WINDOW

Then the warriors excused themselves, saying: "It is not seemly for grown men to fight with a beardless youth!" But Mave called two woman-bands, who went and told Cuculain that sport was made of him for that he had no beard. So Cuculain took a handful of grass and daubed himself a beard. And he came up on a knoll overlooking the men of Erin, and made that beard manifest. "Behold!" then urged the women, "Cuculain hath a beard!"

And now the men of Erin broke faith of fair fight with Cuculain. They sent twenty men against him, fearful to fight him alone; and Cuculain was sorely wounded, and dragged himself out of the combat and sat alone in distress. And he saw far away the fiery glitter of golden arms on the heads of four of the five grand provinces of Erin, in the setting of the sun, in the purple clouds of evening. But thereafter Cuculain slept till the end of three days and three nights; for from Monday before Summer-end, to Wednesday after Spring-beginning, Cuculain had not slept except for a brief snatch at mid-day, leaning against his spear.

And while he slept came the boy-troop from Emain Macha to help him. They took their little play-clubs, and came against the men. Three battles they offered the hosts until every boy was slain! And when Cuculain awoke and heard of the slaughter of his boy-troop, behold, the torches of the war-fury flashed in mists from his head, and so he fared forth to avenge them.

Then the men of Erin took counsel who could be sent to the ford to the combat with Cuculain, and they chose one Ferdiad, dear foster-brother of Cuculain. And Ferdiad much misliked to fight his well-loved comrade; but the wily Warrior-Queen brought him to her tent, and Finnabair sat at his side. And Finnabair placed her hand on every goblet he drank; she gave him three kisses with every cup. She passed him sweet-smelling apples over the bosom of her tunic, and she ceased not to say that he was her darling and sweetheart, her chosen of all the world's men!

And Cuculain was sorely grieved and he said: "As my soul liveth I wish not to fight with Ferdiad for the love and affection I bear him!" But since he needs must fight, Cuculain, that feat-performing, battle-winning, red-sworded hero, mounted his chariot boldly, so that there shrieked around him the goblins, fiends, and sprites of the glens, that the terror of him might be greater.

The two heroes met at the ford and each reproached the other by reason of past friendship; yet each hurled weapons at the other from morning's twilight till noon, and from the middle of noon till yellowness came over the sun at the hour of evening's sun-down; but at nightfall when they ceased fighting, each put his hand on the other's neck, and gave to him three kisses in remembrance of fellowship. Their horses fed in one paddock that night; their charioteers sat at one fire; and they shared all food between them.

So for three days they fought, and for three nights parted in friendship, but when the fourth day dawned, each knew that the end had come. The two heroes, the two champions, bright torches of valor of the Gael, were set to slay each other through sowing

FROM THE TOWER WINDOW

of dissension by wiles of Ailill and Queen Mave. And when the mid-day came, the rage of each grew wild! Cuculain arose with the dash of a dragon into the clouds of the air to leap on Ferdiad's shield and strike his head from above,—but Ferdiad gave the shield a violent, powerful shake, so Cuculain flew far from it into the middle of the ford. With the swiftness of a swallow and the wail of the storm-wind playing in the rafters of the firmament, Cuculain arose again and smote Ferdiad with his spear.

"I die," sighed Ferdiad. Then Cuculain, wounded sorely, clasped Ferdiad in his arms and bore him over the ford; and he said: "What availeth life to me now that this one falls by my hand?"

And a cloud and a faint and a swoon came over Cuculain there.

Then Sualtam came to comfort his son, and Cuculain said to his father: "Go now to Emain Macha! Awaken the men of Ulster! Bid them have a care for their droves; for no longer am I able to protect them in the gaps and passes of the land!"

Riding on horseback, Sualtam shouted through sleep-dead stillness: "Men are slain; women stolen, cattle lifted, ye men of Ulster!"

No one answered his call! Sleepily the Druids murmured: "Disturb not the sleep of the King!" Yet slowly somewhat pierced through the deadly drowse of the spell, to the mind of Concobar. As one who speaketh in dreams, he whispered: "Prepare for battle!"

Now the messenger of Queen Mave, went to survey the plain, and he heard a rush and a crash, a clatter and a clash, and he hastened to tell Queen Mave. And Mave cried: "What hath he heard?" And Fergus answered: "This,—he hath heard the rush and tramp, the din and thunder of Ulstermen coming into battle!" And again the messenger looked, and he saw a heavy gray mist dotted with shining stars as on clear nights of hoar-frost. And Mave cried: "What hath he seen?" And Fergus answered: "This,—he hath seen the breath of horses, the smoke of dusty roads beaten by horses' hoofs! And these are the shining stars that glitter through the mist, even the terrible eyes of the champions of Ulster!"

How rise the Ulstermen now! Manfully do they rise!

"Alas that I may not join them!" Cuculain cried in sorrow chafing against his wounds as he lay there on the ground. Thrice from the north the battle went against Concobar, against the men of Ulster. Then Cuculain uttered a shout, a deafening, ear-splitting shout, and he gave a mighty spring so the bindings of his wounds flew from him as far off as Connaught! And he came into battle at noonday and he fought with the strength of an hundred. And by the ninth hour when the sun entered the tresses of the wood, when in the twilight man and tree were no more to be known apart, Mave and her last company fled before him over the hills. Only Finnabair Fairbrow, Finnabair, lure of warriors, Cuculain took his prisoner, and her he made his bride. Then Concobar and his nobles sang their praise of Cuculain, he who had battled so long, one alone against many, in bold defense of his land.

But as regards Queen Mave, she let not her hosts disperse; she led them forth to behold the battle of the bulls. When the Brown Bull sighted the White-horned, there was a pawing and digging, a bellowing and roaring; the eyes of the bulls blazed red and each gave resounding blows. That night the bulls coursed over the greater part of Erin; the Brown Bull slew the White-horned and gave forth three of the chiefest bellowings of his throat in mighty boast of his triumph. He drank three rivers dry, and ran on home to Coolney, where his heart broke in his breast. So ended the Cow-raid of Coolney, and Cuculain's most daring deed.

FROM THE TOWER WINDOW

The Wanderings of Aeneas

An Epic of the Romans retold from the Latin of Virgil

In ages gone, the Greeks for ten long years besieged great Troy, whereto King Priam's son, the thieving Paris, bore his stolen Helena, the wife of Sparta's King, and so by wanton selfishness, brought down upon his sire, his country and his friends the woes of war. And in those days, no Trojan hero, save great Hector, bore himself more nobly in the fray than goddess-born Aeneas, son of old Anchises and fair Venus, Queen of Love. Strong-hearted in defense of home and hearth, Aeneas fought until the wily Greeks pretending flight, yet left upon the Trojan plain a wooden horse, which when the men of Troy had been induced by trickery to drag within the walls, disgorged by night a hidden throng of Greeks to open up the city-gates, let in their fellow-Greeks, and so bring down that one last night of horror on sad Troy.

It was the hour when heaven's first gift of sleep on weary hearts of men most sweetly stole; but shrieks and loud confusion swept the town till unto that far dwelling where Aeneas slept, embowered in trees, the din drew near and battle-thunder swelled. Aeneas woke and starting from his couch, climbed to his roof-top and its

The story of Dido and Aeneas is told in the opera *Dido and Aeneas*, by the English composer, Henry Purcell (1658-1695). This first and greatest English opera, forgotten for many years, is now becoming popular again.

tower, then stood with listening ear like some stray shepherd on a distant cliff, who hearkens dumb with fear while far away he hears a mountain-stream that bursts in flood and overwhelms sweet fields and farms. Shrill trumpets rang; loud voices roared, and all the air resounded high as heaven with shouts of war. Then wildly ran Aeneas to the fight. Beneath the pale moon, see! The whole vast horde of Greeks swarms in the town. With fronting spears they throng each narrow street, their steel-bright blades all flashing naked, while the battle-flames leap high.

"To arms, my men! To arms!" Aeneas cried and roused his Trojan friends to join his band, till past the foemen's steel they forced their way, while wings of night above them brooded in one sad vast vault of shade. But who the bloodshed of that night can tell? The ancient city fell. Along her streets were strewn the unresisting dead; at household shrines and by the temples of the gods they lay. Then all the roar and tumult led Aeneas and his friends unto King Priam's palace where so fierce a battle raged it seemed as if save this, there were no other conflict known. By secret way Aeneas and his band go in to join the throng who guard the doors; for there Troy's dying brave make one last stand and seek a warrior's death. But spite of all, assailing Greeks break down the door and swarming in, do butchery, while through the vista of long courts and corridors, confusion, groans, and turmoil rise. From many a dark retreat the women shriek and wail! Their loud cries strike the stars. The old Queen Hec'u-ba and all the princesses take refuge vain before a shrine, close-gathering there like panic-stricken doves in some dark storm, while seeing thus his kingdom lost, the aged King himself doth bind his rusted armor on, resolved to die encircled by the foe. Then to the shrine one stalwart son, pursued and wounded unto death, comes plunging in sad flight; the father weakly hurls his spear at him who follows in pursuit; but lo, the Greek, in cold disdain doth clutch the old man's tresses gray and bury deep his sword in that defenseless heart!

FROM THE TOWER WINDOW

Then first wild horror on Aeneas fell and dazed him utterly. As thus he saw old Priam die, a vision rose before his inward eye of his own cherished father, and his wife and little son, in danger left at home. He longed a warrior's death to find, but in that moment, wild with woe, he saw with vision clear in golden beams that pierced the midnight gloom, his goddess-mother, lovely Venus stand with all that mien of majesty she wore in heaven itself, while from her lips of rose this counsel fell: "Fly, O my son! The war's wild work is o'er. Anchises, thine old father thou must save, and her, thy wife, Cre-ü'sa, and As-ca'ni-us, thy son!"

So went Aeneas to his home; but lo, his sire whom first of all he sought and first would bear to safe asylum in the distant hills, vowed he would never, after fall of Troy, live longer on or bear an exile's woe. In vain Creüsa begged, and small Ascanius. Anchises still cried, "No!" and clung to where he sat nor would be moved until a wonder fell. On young Ascanius' head, a tongue of flame appeared and harmless o'er his tresses played, while suddenly with deafening thunder-peal, cleaving the blackness of the vaulted sky, a meteor-star in trailing splendor ran, exceeding bright. Then old Anchises cried in holy awe: "Gods of my fathers, what a sign! Through him, Ascanius, the gods do promise thus a glorious future for our name! I yield, dear son, and journey at thy side!"

Aeneas then gave orders that the servants of his house, each by a separate way, should go to meet him at a ruined shrine to Ceres, which lay deserted, a little mound beneath an ancient cypress' shade outside the city-gates. He bowed his shoulders broad, o'erspread him with a lion's tawny skin, and lifted old Anchises on his back, entrusting to the old man's care the little images of all their household gods, and taking by the hand his infant son, while at safe distance fair Creüsa followed in the rear. Through shadows then they crept, while he who once had viewed undaunted every instrument of war and all the gathered Greeks in grim array, now shook at every gust and heard all sounds with fevered fear,

alarmed for him, the old man whom he bore, and him, the little son who clasped his hand and with such toddling steps must run to keep his father's stride. So when they came to Ceres' hallowed hill, they found the servitors all gathered there. One person only came not to that meeting place,—Creüsa, young and fair and so beloved, alas, she came not! O alas! Entrusting then his sire and son unto the deep dark shadows of a slanting vale, Aeneas hurried back to that doomed town and offered once again his life to perils without end, in searching for his wife. From street to street he ran with anguish vain; and on Creüsa piteously he called, awaking naught but echoes lone and sad. What dark disaster had befallen her? Alas, he never more did look on her alive! Until the dawn he searched, but when the morning star above the crest of tall Mt. Ida rose, chief in the front of day, he joined his friends again, much wondering to find a mighty multitude assembled there, for exile bound and looking unto him to be their leader and their guide. So, yielding up his grief and lifting once again his aged sire, he fled for refuge to the distant hills; and there while Troy in smouldering ashes lay, the refugees built ships beneath the shade of fair Mt. Ida's peak.

FROM THE TOWER WINDOW

As soon as smiled the light of summer's prime, Anchises, much revered for wisdom of the seer, cried: "Let the sails be spread!" And through his tears, Aeneas saw recede his native shore, the haven and the plains where once was Troy. An exile on the seas, with son and followers and Troy's great guardian-gods, he took his way. By Thrace they pass and Delos' sacred isle. On Crete they land; but there the while Aeneas sleeps, the sacred images of Trojan gods, which through the flames he bore from burning Troy, now seem to rise and stand before him, bathed in silver beams that from the great full moon stream through the latticed wall. These tell him plainly that their true abode, the second Troy, shall be in that far land called Italy, and nowhere else, and there shall spring of Trojan-born Aeneas' race, a man to found great Rome, imperial mistress of the earth, and set Aeneas' name in glory mid the stars!

And so again with spreading sails, Aeneas coursed in hollow ship the spacious sea and past the many isles of Greece he sped until the sun rolled through the years' full circle, and the waves, no longer safe and fair with lightly-whispering breezes o'er their tranquil plain, were rough with icy winter's northern gales. And then it chanced one morn when from the sky Aurora's purple warned away the stars, that lying very low along the far horizon dim, they saw the hills of Italy, and cried with shouts of joy; "Italia, hail!" the while Anchises wreathed a bowl with flowers and from the ship's high stern poured wine into the sea in offering to the gods.

But now they hear from far the crash of shouting seas and shoot to skyward on the arching surge, then dropping deeper than the grave they sink, while round about thrice bellow those vast cliffs of Scylla's fearful strait that lies 'twixt Italy and Sicily's fair isle. Now thrice they see the spouted foam and showers of stars; then wind and sun do fail, and weary, worn, not witting of their way, they drift away from Italy and round the shores of Sicily where dread Mt. Aetna's throat with roar of frightful ruin thunders nigh, uplifting globes of flame with monster tongues that lick the stars. And when on Sicily's far shore they land, alas, Anchises, worn by stormful seas, sole comfort of Aeneas' grievous doom, Anchises dies. His body to the earth they give and with dark offerings dire, build altars sorrowful. Nor do they turn once more with hearts of hope toward Italy, ere Juno, Queen of gods, who ever did pursue the Trojans with wild hate because her rival, Venus, favored them, now feared that Venus' very son Aeneas, might reach Italy and there build up a new and greater Troy. In anger now, unto the storm-cloud land she goes, where pent in chains and bastions strong, the warring winds make empty mountains roar, as wild, they chafe against their bonds, while from a throne of lofty crag, great Ae'o-lus, their King, with sceptred hand, allays their fury and their rage confines. To Aeolus, the angry Juno cries: "Uprouse thy gales! Strike that proud Trojan navy down! Hurl far and wide and strew the waves with dead!" And Aeolus, obedient to his Queen, smites with his spear the hollow mountain's wall.

Then rush the winds through that wide breach in long, embattled lines, and sweep tumultuous from land to land, with brooding pinions o'er the waters spread. Vast billows shoreward roll! The shout of mariners is heard, and creak of cordage, while low-hanging clouds conceal from Trojan eyes all sight of heaven and day. Night o'er the ocean broods; from sky to sky the thunders roll and ceaseless lightnings glare! Aeneas groans and raises both his hands in prayer; but still the waves up-surge! Three ships are wrecked. The lonely swimmers breast the wave, and on the waste of waters wide, weapons of war are seen with spars and planks and treasures rare, that once were Troy's proud boast.

Meanwhile, how all his smitten ocean moaned, the ocean's god, great Neptune, knew; and with indignant mien uplifted o'er the sea his sovereign brow.

"Proud Aeolus may play the King in yon close-bounded prison-house of storms!" he cried. "But yet he doth not rule my sea!"

He spoke and swifter than his word, he harnessed to his azure car his raging steeds with wild white manes, then skimmed along the crested waves with all his train of nymphs, sea-beasts and whales, while there before his path the rolling billows ceased, and storm-clouds fled away. So ceased the seas' uproar, and all the wave-worn Trojan crew on coast of Africa to harbor sailed, and flung their dripping limbs along the ground in passionate longing for the touch of land, while great Aeneas, once again their mournful mood consoled, and stretched at ease on couch of simple green, they rallied their lost powers and feasted well on seasoned wine and haunch of game. And when the cheerful dawn upon him broke, Aeneas, taking with him one sole friend, set out to make a survey of this land where wind and wave had driven him; for desert land of sand it seemed.

But now it chanced that there were rising near, the walls of Carthage, new-built citadel of Dido, that fair queen who recently from Tyre had fled. Si-chae'us, her dear husband, had been richest of all Tyrian lords. But when the kingly power in Tyre unto Pyg-ma'li-on, Dido's brother, came, that wicked wretch, all blinded by his greed, did murder foul upon Sichaeus, and long hid the deed, while with false hopes of her dear lord's return, fair Dido he deceived. But as Queen Dido slept, her husband's ghost before her came and told the tale, then counselled her to fly, self-banished from her ruined land, while for her journey's aid, he whispered where his buried treasure lay, a weight unknown of silver and of

gold. Thus rallying to her cause her friends, Queen Dido sailed away and landed there in Africa, where for a price she bought so much of Afric soil as one bull's hide could measure round.

Meanwhile, Aeneas and his friend, soon climbed the brow of that high hill which overlooked the town. And there where lately naught but Africa's rude cabins rose, Aeneas saw the smooth wide ways, the bastioned gates; he heard the uproar of the throng, while Tyrians toiled unwearied, lifting ponderous stones for wall or citadel, or laying firm the base of their great theatre, as busy bees above a field of flowers in early summer amid sunbeams toil.

Deep in the city's heart there stood a grove of beauteous shade, where Dido had upraised a temple to great Juno, and thereto Aeneas made his way to wait the coming of the Queen, while all the mighty temple he admired and saw thereon, in carvings fair, those well-remembered scenes of Troy's great war, now told upon men's lips the whole world round. And while he stood lost deep in memory, Queen Dido to the shrine in lovely majesty drew near, a throng of youthful followers pressing round her way in bright processional. As fair as lithe Diana, tallest of her train, did Dido pass among her subjects, not less bright her gracious joy while she approved her kingdom's pomp and vast emprise; and then

FROM THE TOWER WINDOW

beneath the temple's vaulted dome she took her place encompassed by armed men, and lifted high upon a throne. And now to his amaze, Aeneas saw there suing at her throne, those comrades whom he had deemed lost in shipwreck on the deep. They told the Queen of him, Aeneas, and his deeds, and Dido cried: "O that the storm which brought you here, had likewise brought your King!"

So did Aeneas cry: "Behold the man you seek! For I am he, Aeneas, Trojan-born!"

And as Queen Dido saw him there, she felt her heart stand still, and thrilled again to hear what great adventures had befallen him. She bade Aeneas welcome 'neath her royal roof and sent the Trojans on the shore a score of bulls, a hundred bristling swine, and lambs to make a feast, while great Aeneas sent her gifts from his tall ships,—a gold-embroidered cloak, a crown of jewels, a sceptre and a necklace of round pearls. Then in her ample court, Queen Dido bade a feast be spread, and had the table set with massive silver, gold-embossed, whereon were graved the mighty deeds of all her sires. And now Aeneas and his band of Trojan chivalry at social feast on lofty pillowed couches lay. Deft slaves fresh water on their fingers poured and from reed-woven basketry renewed the plenteous bread or brought smooth table linen of soft weave. Some fifty handmaids served or at the altars bright,

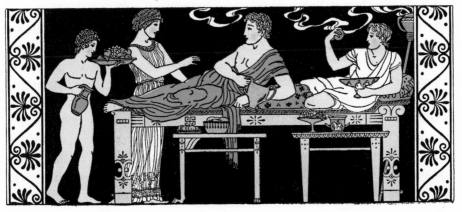

threw balm and incense on the sacred fires, while full an hundred beauteous pages kept the generous board piled high, and filled the bowl. As Dido with Aeneas talked, the dear name of her husband, dead Sichaeus, 'gan to fade and once again her heart went beating new with life and love. And when the main part of the feast was done, the servitors replaced the banquet with huge bowls and crowned the wine with ivy-leaf and rose. Loud rang the roof with echoing voices; from the gilded vault far-blazing cressets swung or torches bright drove night away. The Queen herself called for her golden chalice studded round with jewels, out poured the sacred drop due to the gods, then lightly from the rim the first taste sipped and passed the foaming bowl along. On gilded lyre a minstrel sang and last, to crown the night, Aeneas all his tale of wanderings told.

Thereafter, as her love grew warm, Queen Dido round her cities' battlements did guide Aeneas, to make show of all the wealth her realm could boast, or in his honor gave a royal hunt in sylvan shades. Aurora, goddess of the dawn, had scarcely left her saffron couch and put the morning star to flight, when from the city's gates poured forth a gallant train of huntsmen with their woven snares and steel-tipped javelins, while to and fro ran lean, keen-scented dogs and Libyan squires. Before Queen Dido's door her nobles waited and her palfrey, brave in gold and purple housing, pawed the ground and fiercely champed the foam-flecked bridle-rein. At last with numerous escort forth she shone, her quiver gold, her tresses bound with gold, her robes of purple rare. To meet her came Aeneas, handsome as Apollo, and as dignified of mien.

Soon to the mountains tall, the cavalcade came nigh, to pathless haunts of woodland creatures, where they saw wild goats from pointed crags leap down, and in the vales below they routed deer that scoured the spreading plain and massed their dust-blown squadrons in wild flight. The boy, Ascanius, flushed with sport, spurred on a mettled steed; and many a flying herd his chase outsped; but in his heart he prayed among these tamed things suddenly to see a tusky boar or, wild escaping from the hills in all its savage strength, a growling mountain-lion, golden-maned. Meanwhile, low thunders in the distant sky muttered confusedly; soon burst in full the storm-cloud and the hail. The Tyrian troops were scattered wide. The chivalry of Troy sought shelter where they could, while down the deep ravines the swollen torrents roared. In that same hour Queen Dido and her hero out of Troy unto one cavern fled and while they waited there 'mid lightning's flash, they plighted troth as lovers may.

Thenceforth all winter long they passed in revel and at ease, naught heeding she of crown or he of kingdom, thinking only of their love. But Jove, great King of gods, was angered this to see, and calling to him Mercury, the messenger of Heaven, he sent him over land and sea on those winged sandals that outrace the wind, to bid Aeneas call to mind the task the gods had set him, how in Italy he was to find Troy's gods a home and build a kingdom that should rule the earth in justice and in peace. To clay-built Punic huts the god drew nigh and there he saw Aeneas, destined of the gods to found the Roman race, now building walls for Carthage, while he wore a purple mantle, 'broidered fair by Dido with fine threads of gold, her gift of love. "Why lingerest thou?" cried Mercury. "Hast thou forgotten Italy and Rome?"

Aeneas heard and as one waking out of dreams, his task recalled. He must go on. His duty bade. He could not linger here! But O alas! how should he break such news unto the Queen who loved him so? He bade his men to fit the fleet all silently while he should wait a time, most favorable to speak of parting to the Queen.

But what can cheat true love? The Queen fore-knew his plan. Distractedly she raved and to Aeneas cried: "Is it from me thou takest flight? O by these flowing tears thy purpose change!"

But he, obeying Jove's decree, gazed steadfastly away; and in his heart with strong repression crushed his cruel pain. "O

Queen," he cried, "the thought of thee will be my treasure long as memory holds! Not of my wish I go; the gods themselves command me on!"

Still Dido with wild words reproached him more, and sick at heart she fled the light of day, in her own marble chamber shut from human eyes. Soul-stirred with sorrow, sad Aeneas sat. His heart was weak with woe; he yearned to soothe her misery, her grief, her loss; yet held his purpose fast, to carry through his task.

The Trojans push into the sea their lofty ships,—Behold them how they haste! And Dido, how her suffering heart was wrung as from her towering citadel she saw the shore alive, the sea itself in turmoil with loud cries. "Their canvas woos the winds, and o'er each prow the merry seamen hang their votive flowers!" she cried. And so she bade be built for her a lofty funeral pyre within a quiet garden's shade and high thereon to heap Aeneas' arms, his robes and sword. Then when she from her battlements beheld the sky grow bright with dawn, and great Aeneas' mated sails push forth to sea, till all her port and strand held not an oar or keep, she smote her lovely breast and rushing to the garden climbed the pyre where with Aeneas' sword she slew herself. And as her maidens and her sister Anna, grieving came, the flames shot up from that sad funeral pyre, and Iris, goddess of the rainbow, came on dewy saffron pinions down from heaven, shedding forth a thousand colors on her way, to set the spirit of the sad Queen free.

FROM THE TOWER WINDOW

Meanwhile Aeneas with his fleet kept on his course into the open sea; but when his eyes looked back on Carthage, he beheld the glare of hapless Dido's fire. Not yet was known what kindled those wild flames; yet sad foreboding shook each Trojan soul.

"He triumphs over Fortune who endures through all she brings," Aeneas said, and sailed away. Upon a shining morn when sudden calm possessed the air, and tides of marble smoothness met the laboring oar, he, gazing from the deep, beheld again the shores of Italy, a stretch of groves, whence Tiber's smiling stream, its tumbling current rich with yellow-sands, burst seaward forth, while round it and above shore-haunting birds of varied voice and plume flattered the sky with song, and circling over-head, took joyful wing. Thither to landward now his ships he steered and sailed, high-hearted, up the shadowy stream.

Here in the tranquil vales and towns, the aged King Latinus held his sway and having now no son, he held one daughter only, fair Lavinia, as heir to all the vast possessions which he owned. Full many suitors wooed the maid but comeliest in all their princely throng came Turnus, of a line of mighty sires. Him the Queen-Mother chiefly loved and yearned to call her son. But omens dire from heaven withstood her will; upon a sacred laurel-tree within the palace gates, there settled from afar a swarm of bees, and as Lavinia offered sacrifice before the household shrine, there burned a sudden weird unearthly flame along her flowing hair.

"Seek not in wedlock with a Latin lord to join thy daughter,"
said the oracle divine. "There comes for her a husband from afar,
as came the bees; and as the fire about her head so shall her glory
be. His son and hers shall bear thy name in glory to the stars!"

To this advice Latinus gave much heed, and when there came to
him ambassadors from great Aeneas, newly-landed on his shore, he
cried: "Aeneas is the man the oracle foretold;" and straightway
offered him Lavinia as bride. But even here on the Italian shore,
cruel Juno still pursued Aeneas with her hate. She put wild anger
in the hearts of Turnus and the Mother-Queen. Now in the leafy
dark of mountain-vales the mother hides her daughter, fair Lavinia,
away, and with fierce frenzy stirs the people up to war, while Turnus, summons all his chiefs and bids them thrust Aeneas from the
land. Long raged the war, and mighty were the exploits done,
till on a day, young Turnus fell before the great Aeneas' sword.
Then to the bridals with Aeneas fair Lavinia was brought, that
here upon Italia's shore might rise that mighty race whence Romu-
lus would come and found imperial Rome, to rule the world. And
thus the great Aeneas did endure through dangers and temptations all, and so fulfill most faithfully his purpose and his task.

Arms and the hero I sing who first from the shores of the Trojans,
Fleeing, sharp-driven by fate, to Italy came and Lavinia.
Much had he suffered on land; much tossed had he been on the ocean,
Fleeing the wrath of cruel Juno and seeking to found him a city;
Bringing his father's gods to settle them safely in Latium,—
Latium whence came the Latins and wide-walled, imperial Roma.

FROM THE TOWER WINDOW

The Home-Coming of Odysseus

Retold from The Greek Epic, The Odyssey by Homer

IN manhood's prime, Odysseus went with all the mighty men of Greece to conquer Troy. For ten long years he labored to reduce great Troy, and when that work was done, still ten years more must wander o'er the deep, laboring 'gainst wind and wave, to bring his comrades safely home, and ever longing in his heart for fair Penelope, his wife, and sweet Telemachus, his little son. Oft was he tempest-tossed and cast upon strange, savage shores, now where that fierce, man-eating Cyclops dwelt, now where the cruel enchantress Circe turned his men to beasts, and now in that sleep-laden land where eaters of the lotus flower did tempt unwary men to waste their days in dreams. And when he had o'erpassed these dangers all, his ship was wrecked, and he was borne, the sole survivor of his men, upon the shores of fair Calypso's Isle.

The bright-haired nymph Calypso found the storm-worn hero on the beach and led him to the grotto where she dwelt, a lovely spot hid far in depth of greenery with sparkling crystal springs. Calypso made the days to pass in joy, and there awoke within her heart a love for this wise hero, cast by shipwreck on her shore, nor would she lend her aid to find him any boat wherein he might once more embark upon the deep. Then went Odysseus to the craggy rocks that edged the shore and there sat sorrowing alone, as with his tear-wet eyes he gazed far off across the sea, and wished that he might conjure up a well-oared galley, flying swift before the wind, to take him home.

While thus Odysseus yearned and sorrowed on Calypso's Isle, in high Olympus met the gods who guide affairs of men; and great Athene, light of wisdom unto human kind and fond protectress of the sage Odysseus, sought her father, Zeus, high-thundering on his throne of power, to plead Odysseus' cause

217

before the King of Gods. And Zeus sent Hermes, his swift-footed son and messenger, to bid Calypso aid Odysseus in the building of a raft, and leave him free to start once more upon his wished-for journey home.

O'er land and sea did Hermes fly and down he plunged unto the deep, to skim its surface like a hovering seamew that will often dip her pinions in the waves. Soon he perceived Calypso's cave. A fire burned brightly on the hearth, and far was wafted o'er the isle the fragrant smoke of cloven cedar burning in the flame, and cypress-wood. Meanwhile in her recess, the nymph was sitting at her loom, and singing sweetly as full busily she threw the golden shuttle through the web she wove.

"Zeus sends me to thee, nymph," swift Hermes said, "to bid thee send Odysseus hence with speed."

With words of woe Calypso wailed her lot, but since none could withstand the purposes of Zeus, she yielded up her will and promised to obey. She sought Odysseus out and told him how she meant to give him means to build a raft, but ah! she cautioned him if he but knew through what great dangers he must pass, not all his longing for Penelope and home would ever lead him forth to face them all. Yet that great-hearted hero said, "Let come what will, I go; for in my bosom dwells a mind patient of suffering; how much I have endured and much survived in tempests on the deep and in the battle; let this happen too!"

Now when the Child of Dawn, Aurora, rosy-fingered, looked abroad, Odysseus donned his mantle; and the nymph, Calypso of the amber hair, robed all in silver-white with golden girdle at her waist and filmy veil out-floating, lightly resting on her head, gave axe and adze unto the hero and led him to that corner of the woods where grew the tallest trees.

FROM THE TOWER WINDOW

Two score tall trees Odysseus felled; he squared their trunks and smoothed their sides and built himself a raft, with woven work of willow boughs to guard its sides against the dashings of the sea. Then came Calypso bringing canvas and stout ropes wherewith he rigged a sail, and thus his vessel all complete, he launched it on the deep. Calypso gave to him a skin of dark red wine, a skin of water, and a basket stored with choicest viands; and Odysseus, bidding her farewell, cast loose his moorings as he spread his canvas joyfully to catch the breeze.

For seventeen long days he fared in safety on his craft, until the far Phaeacian shores came full in sight, where it had been foretold his sorrows should at last come to an end. But now Poseidon, ruler of the sea, who held Odysseus ever in enmity, saw him at last about to land and so escape forever from the realm he ruled; and in fierce wrath, Poseidon urged his steeds with flowing manes on through the deep to where Odysseus stood. He spake, and round about him called the clouds; he roused the ocean, wielding in his hand the trident, summoned all the hurricanes of all the winds, and covered earth and sky at once with mists, while from above the night fell suddenly. A huge and frightful billow from on high crashed down and whirled the raft around, the while it washed Odysseus from the deck. A savage rush of all the winds together snapped the mast in twain; the yard and canvas flew far off into the deep. The billow held the hero long beneath the waters, but struggling through the waves at last, he reached his battered craft and sprang once more on board. As thus he clung, a silver-footed nymph beheld him, and in pity, rose up from the deep, to perch upon his raft, in form a great white bird. "Let go thy raft," she cried, "and swim for the Phaeacian shore."

Odysseus heard and plunged obediently into the deep. Two days and nights among the stormy waves he floated valiantly, but on the third day reached a rocky shore with beetling crags and walls of rock, against which he was well-nigh crushed to death. Then just in time he came upon a smooth and quiet shore within a little cove, and there he crept up on the beach and found a pleasant wood that crowned a height above a stream. Within the wood he heaped up for himself a couch of leaves, flung down his wearied limbs, and slept.

And while Odysseus rested there, Athene, his protecting goddess, planned a way whereby she might send fair Nausicaa, the daughter of Phaeacia's King, to find the hero in his resting place and bring him safely to her father's home. Assuming now the form of one of those young maids who served Nausicaa, Athene spake:

"Nausicaa, has then thy mother brought thee forth a careless housewife? Thy marriage day is not far off, and yet the garments thou hast all prepared have not been washed. Tomorrow with the dawn, make suit to thine illustrious father that he bid his mules and car be harnessed to convey thy girdles, robes, and mantles to the washing place, where we will wash them clean."

Nausicaa, thus prompted, with the morning light arose and went to seek her parents. By the hearth her mother turned her distaff 'midst her maids; her father on the threshold was preparing to go forth and meet his chiefs in council. Modestly the maiden proffered her request, and soon, obedient to the King's command, the servitors made ready in the outer court the strong-wheeled chariot, and led the harnessed mules beneath the yoke. Within the polished car, Nausicaa and her maidens gaily piled the shining garments, while the good Queen-Mother filled a hamper full of pleasant meats and flavored morsels for the day's repast. Nausicaa then lightly climbed into the car, seized in her hands the scourge and shining reins, and urged the good mules forward, while her maidens trooped with merry laughter round the wain.

FROM THE TOWER WINDOW

Now when they reached the river's pleasant brink, they loosed the mules to browse upon the grass, and took the garments out to fling them in the stream, thereafter trampling them with hasty feet in frolic rivalry, as was the manner then of washing clothes. And when the task was done, and all the garments cleansed, they spread them out along the beach to dry. In sportive mood, they bathed themselves within the river, splashing sparkling jets of spray in one another's faces, mischievous in mimic battle. Then donning once again their robes, they spread their noonday meal upon the grass beside the river's brink, and ate of it with busy buzz of maidens' talk and laughter. And when they thus were rested and refreshed, they cast their filmy veils aside and played at ball. Now here, now there, the little ball went flying through the air, while all those lithe and graceful figures leapt and swayed and bounded, twinkling in the light.

At length, white-armed Nausicaa flung back her hand and cast her ball at one of her young maids; but missing aim, it went beyond the maid and fell into a whirling eddy of the stream. Then all those pretty players shrieked aloud, and by that sound Odysseus was awakened from his sleep. Arising from his couch of leaves, he issued from the thicket, hair unkempt and clothes in rags, like to some wild man, half a beast. At unexpected sight of such a savage stranger, all the maidens fled. White-armed Nausicaa alone maintained her place, and unto her Odysseus told his tale, beseeching pity, while he begged that she should give him some old robe wherein to wrap himself, and lead him to the town. Much moved, Nausicaa cried: "The stranger and the poor are sent by Zeus!" She bade her maidens bring a cloak and tunic with a cruse of oil, and then to leave the stranger there to cleanse and clothe himself. And when Odysseus had anointed all his limbs with oil, and donned the garments she had given, he appeared of such a stately size and such majestic mien, that fair Nausicaa knew well his tale was true. Behind her car, now laden

with the fresh-washed linen and attended by those pretty maids in graceful train, Odysseus walked. She bade him follow her until they came nigh to the town, and then, lest men should jeer at seeing him, a man, amidst her crowd of maids, she bade him wait within a little poplar grove outside the walls and make his further way alone.

As thus he passed the city-gate, Athene cast a cloud of darkness over him, that no rude dwellers in the city should do him any harm. Unseen, but seeing, he beheld wondering, the haven and the gallant ships, the market-place where heroes thronged the halls, long, lofty and beset with palisades.

And so he came at last before the splendid palace of Alcinoüs, King of this pleasant land, nor did that friendly veil of darkness fail to shelter him from curious eyes, until he came where sat the King and Queen, and falling, clasped the good King's knees. Here once again he poured out all his sorry tale.

"O great Alcinoüs," he begged, "send me once more to Ithaca, my home!" Then did the great-souled King raise up the hero, promising protection, as he seated him upon a silver-studded throne.

FROM THE TOWER WINDOW

Next day at dawn, he led Odysseus to the market-place beside the harbor filled with ships. There gathered likewise all the great Phaeacian chiefs, and when Alcinoüs had told them how this nameless stranger sought their aid to take him to the home from which he had so long been torn, it was agreed that all should feast together in his honor for that single day; whereafter they would load the suppliant with gifts and take him home.

There followed then a splendid feast, with singing from the silver tongue of one blind bard, with graceful dancing of the lithe-limbed youths, and feats of wrestling, running, discusthrowing, in the which Odysseus much excelled. When this was done, the good Phaeacians loaded down their guest with gifts; he paid his grateful thanks unto the King and Queen, and was conveyed aboard a well-oared ship. Phaeacian rowers bore him on across the deep until they came to Ithaca, his island-home; and while he slept, they set him and his treasure both on shore and left him sleeping on his native soil without awaiting thanks.

When he awoke, Athene suddenly appeared to tell him news of home. For during those long years that he had been away, his true and faithful wife, Penelope, had been beset by suitors who, against her will, were bent on forcing her to marry one of them, and while they waited, thinking surely that Odysseus must be dead, they filled the hero's palace hall with revellings, and lived in riotous extravagance upon his beeves and swine and wine. Penelope, the faithful, sought from day to day to put off wedding one of them; for in her loyal heart she never yielded up the hope that some day great Odysseus would come home again. Upon her loom, she wove a robe for old Laertes, her good father-in-law, and every day she told the suitors that she would not wed until the robe was done; but every night she raveled out the work that in the day she wove, and so did time pass on. The suitors chafed at her delay, but fair Penelope remained a faithful wife.

Her son, Telemachus, now grown to manhood, had gone forth into the world to seek some certain news of his beloved father, but the suitors hated young Telemachus; for well they knew he kept Penelope from yielding to their suit; and now they planned to lie in wait for him when he returned, and treacherously to slay the youth who hindered their designs. All this Athene told Odysseus, then she changed him to the likeness of a ragged beggar, ordering him to seek his faithful swineherd out, and in his hut plan how to drive the suitors from his home.

The faithful swineherd, though he did not recognize his master under this disguise, received the ragged stranger with a simple courtesy and kindliness, and served him with his best, conversing meanwhile of his love for his departed master, and the greed of those insistent suitors, which was so depleting all Odysseus' flocks and herds. At early dawn Odysseus and the swineherd were preparing food for breakfast when Odysseus saw a youth approach the lodge, on whom the fierce dogs, wont to bark at strangers, now affectionately fawned. When in good time the youth was come

FROM THE TOWER WINDOW

within the hut, the swineherd greeted him full lovingly as young Telemachus, his master, and begged that he would occupy the place of honor at his board. But this Telemachus most modestly declined in favor of the stranger, unto whom in spite of his poor rags, he showed respect.

Odysseus, deeply moved, then told the youth that he was none but that great sufferer, his long lost father, and the youth, impetuous, did throw his arms about him shedding tears of joy, the while Odysseus kissed his son, and from his eyelids, too, though long restrained, the tears fell to the earth. Their first excitement past, Odysseus bade his son go to the palace, there to bide the time to act. And when the day was far advanced, Odysseus in his beggar's rags, unrecognized by all, was led by that true, faithful swineherd to the palace, wherein he entered all alone just as the suitors' wonted revels reached their height and filled the court with noise and song. Alone, he stood before the walls that once had owned him master. None of all whom he had ruled, now knew him, save his hunting dog, cast out upon the dust heap, as too old for life and use. That tried and trusty friend with one last gleam of joy, crept to his master, greeting him, then fell before him dead. An unseen tear Odysseus dropped upon the faithful head of that one friend, as turning he advanced into the palace-hall.

When now he stood within the doors of that vast hall filled full of foes, Odysseus humbly bowed his head and made the round of all the suitors, begging aid of each to try what sort of man he was. The suitors, each more insolent than the rest, heaped insult upon insult on his head, and one, Antinoüs dared fling a stool to strike him down. So angered was Penelope when told of this discourteous act, that she herself came down to ask forgiveness of the stranger, though she knew him not, and to inquire if he by chance had anywhere heard tidings of her lord. How dear to that worn hero, tossed by many storms, was this first sight of his beloved wife, how like sweet music fell her voice upon his ear!

But yet Penelope, though thus she asked so yearningly for news of her dear husband, knew him not.

Save for Telemachus and one old faithful nurse who pierced through his disguise, Odysseus met that night with naught but great discourtesy in his own house, where those proud suitors, swarming like an army, filled the place.

Now that same morning, fair Penelope had said that she would hold a contest for her hand. "Let him among my suitors who can string Odysseus' mighty bow and shoot an arrow through twelve rings to hit the mark, have me to be his bride," she said, and unto this proposal all her suitors eagerly agreed.

First on that festal night, Antinoüs did strive. In vain, he could not bend the bow. Another suitor tried and then another still, but none among them all could even string that bow.

While thus they tried, Odysseus stepped before his foes and boldly cried that he would span the bow. Gibes rose with jeers! How should a ragged beggar think that he could bend Odysseus' mighty bow! The beggar seized the weapon, sent his first shaft true and straight through all twelve rings and struck the mark!

A silence fell. Amazed and thunderstruck were that proud host. And then Odysseus turned about to face his haughty foes, the while he grimly said: "Another goal awaits my second arrow!"

Through the heart he shot the false Antinoüs, yea, in the very act of lifting to his lips a two-eared goblet full of wine. Noise followed with confusion, but the suitors were unarmed; for secretly Odysseus and his son had found a means to take their weapons from them while they drank and thought of naught save foolish revelry. Telemachus sprang forward to his father's side, the swineherd stood on guard before the door, and thus returning day saw not a single one of all those thieving revelers left alive, leech-like to suck his substance from Odysseus' beeves and swine. And on that self-same night, the nurse announced the safe return of great Odysseus to his servants and his wife.

FROM THE TOWER WINDOW

Such news to that long-waiting wife could scarce be credited, and going down to meet the stranger still in beggarly attire, she could not well believe that here her husband stood once more. Odysseus, longing then for dawn of recognition in her fair sweet eyes, proposed that all should purify themselves and sit together for the evening feast. And when Penelope beheld him in his own fair form, dressed once again as he was wont to be, she fell upon his neck in deepest joy, and he, so long lone wanderer o'er the earth, wept grateful tears, as in his arms once more he held his dearly loved and faithful wife. And thus Odysseus came into his own again, to rule his people with that same benignity and wisdom that were his before, or ever he had left fair Ithaca and with his warriors gone to humble distant Troy.

A Story of Rustem, the Hero of Persia

Retold from the Shah—Nameh (Book of Kings) by Firdusi

N THE days when the great Chieftain Saum ruled over the province of Seis-tan' there was born unto him a son named Zal, who had hair as white as a lily, as white as a goose's wing, as white as the snows on the mountain tops. For that reason, though the child's form was straight as a cypress tree, his face in beauty shining like the moon, men laughed at the Chieftain, Saum; and Saum, the hero of many battles, fell conquered as any coward weakling before the taunts and scorn of men. On a night of storm and thunder, he gave commands that his helpless babe should be left to perish on a mountain top.

Now on the border of Seis-tan', far from the homes of men, stands the mountain called Elburz. Its lofty crest towers up to meet the stars; its sides are rocky cliffs so steep that mortal foot hath never scaled them. Here, far, far beyond the reach of men, the Si-murgh' has her nest, the giant bird, the bird of marvel. Of shining ebony, black as night and fragrant sandalwood that nest was builded; around its base the cliffs were thickly veined with golden quartz, and gleamed with rubies, topaz, opals, brilliant stones of fire. From out the swirling banners of storm, a voice addressed the Bird of God and bade her save the babe. Sweeping down she took him gently in her talons and bore him to her nest, there to warm him with her own dear nestlings under her tender golden wings. In her lofty eyrie the Simurgh brought the babe to boyhood. Many a time, at her request he sprang

228

upon her mighty back and was borne in free and glorious flight, up, up to the golden moon, in and out amongst the silvery stars, till he knew all the wonders of the heavens; then sweeping down, down over all the earth, till he knew all the wisdom of men.

But the time came when the lonely Saum repented sorely what he had done, so that even the remembrance of his deeds of valor was but as dust in his nostrils. Then he went to Mt. Elburz, found his son, now grown a youth, bowed his head to the earth before him, and besought him to return unto Seis-tan'. With grief and tenderness, the Silver-Crowned One bade his foster-mother farewell and went back home with Saum. A mighty hero he grew to be to gladden his father's heart, but the greatest moment in all his life was that wherein the Bird of Wisdom, the all-knowing Bird of God, brought unto him and his fair bride Ru-da-beh', a son, a splendid boy whom they called Rus'tem, which meaneth "delivered." "For," said the wise men, "while he liveth, will he ever stand between Persia and her foes."

Now the child was as fair as a nosegay of lilies and tulips and of marvelous strength. At news of his coming the whole land of I-ran' was given over to feasting and rejoicing. Everywhere flowers were flung into the streets, gay Persian carpets were hung from the balconies, and young and old came forth to sing and dance with mirth and music. But the great Saum himself was away at this time, fighting the Deevs of Maz-in'-de-ran, so his son sent swift messengers on wind-footed dromedaries bearing unto him a likeness of Rustem worked in silk, representing the babe on a horse, armed like a warrior and carrying a cow-headed mace. When the old champion beheld this image he was overwhelmed with delight and returned thanks at once unto Or'-muzd for this splendid gift to his house.

The boy waxed daily in strength and intelligence, but not until he was eight years old, might the eyes of Saum be gladdened by the sight of his wonderful grandson. Then, when Saum returned from his wars, Rustem went forth to meet him in the midst of a body-guard mounted on coal black steeds, with golden maces and battle-axes gleaming in the sun, while lords and nobles of the land with waving plumes and splendid banners followed in gaily decked howdahs borne on the backs of elephants, to the squealing of fifes, the blare of trumpets, clash of cymbals and beating of drums.

When Rustem beheld his illustrious grandsire approaching, he dismounted as was meet, and humbly approached on foot, pausing before his elephant, and bowing reverently to the ground. Beholding the youth, Saum was struck dumb with wonder and joy, for he saw that not half had been told him as to the boy's stature and grace. Filled with delight, the old warrior blessed his grandson and bade him ascend into the howdah beside him. Thus the two rode together unto Za-bu'-li-stan'. And Rustem said unto Saum; "O, my grandsire, I rejoice to be grandson to such a doer of deeds as thou. For mine own desires are not after pleasure; neither do I think of play nor rest nor sleep, but ever and always I long to be a hero, performing deeds of valor, defeating those demons of darkness, the Deevs, saving Persia from her foes. And most of all now I crave a horse of mine own and a helmet and coat of mail."

Now Saum was delighted with these words, and ere he left the house of Zal again to go forth to battle he said:

"Remember, my silver-crowned son, when this child's stature equals thine, he is to have a horse of his own choosing, and all the trappings thereto. Honor this as my parting command."

Short and full were the days of Rustem's childhood, filled with many a deed of valor, and he was still but a lad in years, when the great day came whereon Saum decreed he had earned the right to choose his own horse, as had been promised. Accordingly, a proclamation was sent out to all the provinces of Persia, commanding that upon the first day of the approaching Festival of Roses,

all the choicest horses in the land should be brought to Zabulistan that Rustem might choose from among them. Soon the hills without the city grew white with the tents of traders from Ka-bul' and the Af'-ghan pasture-lands, while hordes of half-wild Tar'-tars in black sheepskin caps swarmed over the plains with their herds of dark-maned horses; low-browed men from the Cas'-pi-an, standing erect in their saddles, rode their clean-limbed animals at full speed beneath the city walls, and troops of high-spirited Arab coursers went prancing hither and yon in charge of a dig-nified Sheik of the desert.

On the morning of the Festival of Roses, when the meadows smiled with verdure, filling all the air with fragrance, Zal and Rustem took their seats on a beautiful golden throne just without the western gate midst a throng of people gathered together to see the splendid show. One by one, the mettlesome steeds were led for inspection before the seat of Rustem. Proudly each master approached, but though many a horse was swift and beautiful and gentle, Rustem, the powerful, bore down the weight of his hand on each and not one among them but sank to his haunches from force of that mighty pressure. Crestfallen, his master was forced to lead him away. Alas! so fared it with horse after horse, till keen disappointment filled the soul of Rustem and he knew not what he should do to find a steed to bear him. But, letting his eye rove over the field in one last muster, behold! he suddenly spied beyond the tents of Kabul, a mare and her foal, feeding quietly on the hillside. The mare appeared strong as a lioness, but it was the colt that held Rustem's eye, for its color was that of rose-leaves, scattered on a saffron ground. It appeared as strong as an elephant, as tall as a camel, as vigorous as a lion, and its eyes fairly beamed with intelligence. Seeing this, Rustem cried:

"O sons of Kabul, unto whom belongeth yon splendid colt?"

The herdsmen shook their heads gravely and answered, "Most gracious Prince, we know not. All the way from the Afghan valleys the colt and his mother have followed us, and we could neither drive them back nor capture them. We have heard it said however that the name of the colt is Ra'-kush or Lightning because he is swift as a flash and his spirit is fire. Many have desired to possess him, but in vain. No man hath ever mounted him."

No sooner had Rustem heard this than he seized a lariat from the nearest herdsman, ran quickly forward, and threw the noose without warning over the head of the startled colt. Then followed a furious tussle, not so much with the colt as with the frenzied mother, but lo! the son of Zal strove with such mighty strength that he soon drove the mare from the field. Then he pressed his hand with all his weight down on the colt's back. But Rakush did not even bend under it! So Rustem gave a glad cry, and caressing the creature fondly, said:

"O Rakush! Rakush! verily thou shalt be my throne. Seated on thee I shall do great deeds, my beauty!"

So speaking, with a great bound the young prince leaped

upon his back and the rose colored steed bore him over the plain, with the speed of the wind. But at a single word from his master, Rakush turned and came quietly back to the city gates where the vast crowd was mightily cheering. Then Zal said unto the herdsmen:

"Good herdsmen, what wish ye in exchange for this steed?"

But the herdsmen, turning to Rustem made answer gravely:

"His price is the land of Persia. Mount him and give us in exchange I-ran' delivered from her foes!"

Thus it was that Rustem won his good horse, Rakush, and ever after they two were fast in devotion, loving one another.

Now the chief foes of Persia, in those days, were the Deevs, dark demons who dealt in sorcery. They walked upright like men but had horns, long ears, and tails like beasts and many were cat-headed. Some were small and black, but more were huge and gigantic, and ever the land where they dwelt was a place of illusions and magic. It took the heart of a hero to do battle with such as these.

The Shah over all Persia at that time was one, Kai'-kous, whose riches and power had so increased since he sat on the throne of Light, that he grew puffed up with self-admiration and pride, indulging more and more in the wine cup, until in the midst of his luxury and feasting, he beheld in all the world no man but himself! Then it came to pass one day as the vain Shah sat in his trellised bower in a garden of roses, that a Deev, disguised as a minstrel and playing sweetly upon his harp, presented himself to the King's chamberlain and with honeyed words sought entrance.

Beguiled by the charm of the youth the Chamberlain hastened at once to the King to beg an audience for him.

"O shelter of the Universe," he said, "at thy gate is a minstrel with his harp. And lo! in his throat he hides a flock of singing birds that will make thy bower a paradise. He hath come hither desiring to prostrate himself before the King of Kings, the most illustrious of all the Shahs of Iran, and he awaiteth thy commands, being naught but the dust beneath thy feet!"

The King, blinded by the flattery, so that he perceived no guile, commanded the musician to be brought before him, and the youth, having made obeisance, began to sing of the enchanted land of the genii:

> *"Now thus he warbled to the King**
> *Ma-zin'-de-ran is the bower of spring,*
> *My native home; the balmy air*
> *Diffuses health and fragrance there;*
> *So tempered is the genial glow,*
> *Nor heat, nor cold we ever know;*
> *Tulips and hyacinths abound*
> *On every lawn; and all around*
> *Blooms like a garden in its prime,*
> *Fostered by that delicious clime.*
>
> *The Bulbul sits on every spray,*
> *And pours his soft melodious lay;*
> *Each rural spot its sweets discloses,*
> *Each streamlet is the dew of roses;*
> *The damsels, idols of the heart,*
> *Sustain a most bewitching part.*
> *And mark me, that untravelled man*
> *Who never saw Ma-zin'-de-ran,*
> *And all the charms its bowers possess*
> *Has never tasted happiness!"*

Now as the King's desire was to drain the cup of happiness to the dregs, no sooner had he heard the minstrel's lay of this enchanting land than straightway he became inflamed with the desire to possess it for his own, and declared unto his warriors that they must set forth to conquer it at once. Alas! the nobles when they heard these words of vanity and folly, grew pale with dread, for they had no desire to invade the country of the Deevs. But words were useless to restrain the Shah. Neither the wise counsel of the white-headed Zal would he heed, nor of any other

*The selections from the Shah-Nameh used in this story are from Champeon's translation.

FROM THE TOWER WINDOW

noble. He boasted in answer that naught beneath the sun could withstand the prowess of Kaikous, the Mighty. Ere the week was out the great army of Iran was in motion, the vainglorious King at its head, his magnificent retinue of richly caparisoned horses, camels and elephants, making the earth tremble beneath their tread. So they marched, pitching their tents each night and passing the hours in revelry that ill became those about to do battle with evil. Then the King sent out his bravest warrior, Gew, while he himself remained encamped on the plain at a safe distance from the conflict and he bade Gew break down the gates of the first city in Mazinderan, sparing no man, woman nor child.

So Gew advanced, and when he was come unto the city he found it indeed arrayed in all the splendor of paradise, even as the minstrel had sung. Beauty, verdure, fragrance filled all the senses with delight while gold and jewels glittered everywhere. In the streets were beautiful maidens richly adorned, with faces as bright as the moon. But Gew knew that all this beauty was but the illusion of sorcery and that in truth the Deevs were ugly and foul. He was not, therefore, beguiled. Soon clubs rained down upon the Deevs like hail and ere night had fallen the city that had resembled a garden was become a heap of ruins.

Kaikous was wild with elation at news of the victory that he had done naught to win, and, more puffed up than ever with vanity, he gave command to plunder and pillage, taking thought of nothing at all, save only to slake his greed, and all unworthy the mighty victory over the powers of darkness, which he knew not how to turn to any good account. But over his foolish head hung the sword of vengeance. For the King of Mazinderan, hearing what had happened to one of his mighty cities, sent to the most dreaded and powerful magician in all the land, the Great White Deev, and bade him destroy the men of Iran. And the Great White Deev rose up in wrath and sent a heavy black cloud to envelop the drunken plunderers, causing stones and javelins to rain down on them out of the pitch black sky. All was terror and confusion, nor could any man protect himself. By morning, who was not fled or dead, was stricken stone-blind, and among these latter Kaikous himself. Then came twelve thousand Genii to thrust the blind men into prison. And a voice called out mocking unto Kaikous:

"Verily, O, Shah, thou hast attained Mazinderan which was thy heart's desire, wherefore be now content!"

Thus Kaikous dwelt in the land after which his heart had yearned until, the eyes of his soul being opened in genuine repentance, he bowed himself in the dust, casting black earth upon his head, and acknowledged his fault. Then, and then only, means appeared whereby he might send a messenger unto Zal.

When the Silver-Crowned One heard the sorrowful news, he delayed not, but sent Rustem at once to the rescue. Clad in his tiger-skin and iron helmet, with only his faithful steed for company, the young hero set forth on the perilous journey. Long and difficult was the way, and in many a sore extremity Rakush succored his master, saving him now from a lion, now from a dragon, keeping watch and ward over him while he slept and cheering him ever with faithful comradeship and affection.

So Rustem came at last out of a desert into the land of enchantment, and as everything here was illusion, everything seemed to the eye most beautiful. Feathered palms lazily nodded their heads, bananas flaunted their ribbon-like leaves over clusters of ripened fruit, and on the ground in rich profusion temptingly lay pomegranates, apricots, citrons. In the leaves overhead the nightingale sang, and lo! there suddenly appeared to the astonished sight of the hungry hero a table daintily spread with viands. Unsaddling Rakush and bidding him graze, Rustem sat down to break a long fast, but he ate full temperately and sang as he ate:

> "Oh, the scourge of the wicked am I;
> And my days still in battle go by;
> Not for me is the red wine that flows
> In the reveller's cup, nor the rose
> That blooms in the land of delight,
> But with monsters and demons to fight!"

As Rustem sang, his voice reached the ears of the wicked enchantress who had delayed him with the table, and changing herself into a beautiful maiden with a face of spring she appeared unto him. Her skin was like shell-tinted ivory, her lips and cheeks like the pomegranate, her soft dark eyes curtained with long, sweeping lashes, and her misty garments gave forth such a fragrance that they perfumed all the air. At her approach Rustem was enraptured. She seemed like an houri from paradise, but minding the duties of hospitality he extended to her a goblet, saying, "Drink in the name of Ormuzd[1]."

No sooner had he named the name of God than lo! that wicked sorceress changed color becoming in a twinkling black as coal. Then Rustem knew her for no houri but a witch and he snared her in his lasso crying, "Wicked creature, show thyself in thy true shape!" Whereon he held in his grasp naught but a leering, decrepit, old woman. He smote at her with his sword, but she

[1] The Persian name for God.

slipped from his hand and vanished with mocking, fiendish laughter. Vanished, too, were the table and viands, and Rustem lingered no more, but saddled Rakush and went on his journey.

Now he passed through a land of pitch black darkness and impenetrable gloom, where he knew not what dangers might lurk on either hand. But, lifting up his heart unto Ormuzd for protection and guidance, he gave unto Rakush the rein and plunged boldly forward, emerging at length, thanks to the All-merciful One, into a most beautiful country where the sun was shining. Herein he found one Au'-lad, a chief, and pressed him into his service as guide, by whose aid he came at length to the fateful spot where Kaikous fell into the hands of the enemy. There he beheld the great camp of Ar'-zang, mightiest of all the White Deev's chiefs, and Arzang came boastfully forth to meet him. But in Rustem's heart was neither boasting nor vanity—only sure confidence of the hero, who forgetteth himself and knoweth his cause is just, and he seized the mighty sorcerer like a puny worm in his grasp and slew him and hurled him headlong into the ranks of his own shuddering Deevs, who beholding the fate of their chief, fled, one and all, terror-stricken before the conqueror.

Then Rustem paused not for a moment, but guided by Aulad, pressed on at once to the prison of Kaikous. Great was the joy of Kaikous and his comrades at their deliverance. They offered up thanks to Ormuzd and showered upon Rustem their gratitude. But Kaikous counseled the young hero to proceed at once and slay the Great White Deev in his lair in the Seven Mountains, ere that sorcerer learned of his coming and brought against him such a multitude of Evil ones, that not even Rustem could withstand him. And he told him that three drops of the White Deev's blood in their blinded eyes would recover sight to himself and his miserable companions.

Thus exhorted, the son of Zal vaulted into his saddle and Rakush bore him off like the wind. So they sped till they came

FROM THE TOWER WINDOW

unto the Seven Mountains, dark and terrible, with frowning cliffs and beetling crags and yawning caverns, and everywhere about were crowded myriads of Deevs, fierce, black and horrible beyond belief. Rustem was one against a multitude, yet he waited, wary and watchful, until the Deevs were lost in lazy noonday slumber, when he rushed so fiercely upon them, thundering his battle-cry, that in confusion of their stupid sleep, hundreds fell beneath his sword, while the rest fled panic-stricken into the depths of the earth.

So Rustem advanced in safety to the lair of the Great White Deev. But alas! alas! never in all his imaginings had he dreamed of a place so gloomy and foul—a cavern of pitchy blackness, heavy with evil odors. Yet his heart was strong and he knew no quaking of fear as he made his way forward. In the center of the cave he saw looming up out of the darkness a mighty shape which filled the whole breadth of the cavern and he knew by its thunderous snoring that this was the White Deev himself. Bold as a lion, Rustem shouted his battle cry and sprang at him. Thus suddenly aroused from slumber, the Deev was terrible in his wrath. Uttering a hideous shriek, he rushed upon his foe and they grappled in a struggle, the shock of which caused the very mountains to tremble. Many a time it seemed to Rustem that his last hour had surely come, but lifting up his heart to Ormuzd, and putting forth all his strength, he suddenly caught the huge Deev in his arms and by one supreme effort hurled him over a cliff to his death in the yawning chasm below. Then he possessed himself of some of the White Deev's blood, and returning to Kaikous and his comrades dropped it into their eyes,

239

whereby the enchantment laid on them by the Deev was done away and they received again their sight.

Great as was now the joy of the men of Iran, there still remained to be conquered the King of Mazinderan, who came thundering down upon them with a mighty army, both horse and foot. Long was the struggle with him and many a champion among the magicians Rustem vanquished. Yet the tide of battle was still uncertain. Then Kaikous, changed now in heart by his sufferings from that vainglorious boaster who went forth against the Deevs, clothed himself in robes of humility and prostrated himself before Ormuzd, beseeching that the Kingdom of Light might triumph over the Kingdom of Darkness, and lo! by the evening the Deevs were put to flight and Rustem, pursuing, found the ugly King with his great boar neck and great boar tusks, left all alone, and he challenged him to combat.

Desperately fought the King and coolly fought Rustem. In the end, Rustem raised his sword for such a stroke as would have slain the monster, but in the twinkling of an eye the sorcerer changed himself to a great mass of rock, before which Rustem stood baffled. Kaikous gave orders to his strongest men to drag the rock to his throne. Not all their strength together could even so much as lift it. Then Rustem bent his sturdy back, lifted the rock in his mighty arms and bore it to the Shah. As he cast it down before him, he cried: "Coward, come forth or with my mace I will grind this stone to powder!"

Seeing his trick was useless, the sorcerer quickly made himself visible and Kaikous beholding how wicked was his aspect, ordered him off to immediate execution.

Then Kaikous made Aulad, the guide, King over Mazinderan, after which, with great rejoicing, he and Rustem and all their men went home to Persia. So the tree of gladness blossomed once more in Iran, and because of his mighty victory over the Kingdom of Darkness the name of Rustem stands blazoned among the stars.